guardian
angel

Chapter One

Caught Thinking

"You may find after you've climbed to the top, that your ladder is against the wrong wall."

Anon

THIS ONE MUST HAVE THE SECRET, DOUGLAS THOUGHT as he opened his new purchase. According to the cover notes, it had been written by "one of the world's leading authorities on company change".

Douglas Murray, Chief Executive of *Guardian Angel*, a financial services company offering a wide range of investment, pension and life assurance products, prides himself on keeping up with the latest management innovations. He has in-depth knowledge of Total Quality Management (TQM to those in the know), Business Process Re-Engineering, Empowerment through People and so on. Douglas has written his company's Vision Statement, Mission Statement and Customer Charter. He has also spent considerable sums of money on consultants who have helped flatten the company's management structure in line with current theory, and have introduced new systems to streamline the business. Yet Douglas is still frustrated by the lack of response from his workforce, including his senior managers.

Douglas is small, stocky, and slightly overweight. Although he is 47, some youthfulness can still be seen sneaking out from his well-lived-in face. Dedicated to his work, Douglas arrives at the office each day around 7am. He seldom leaves for home before 7.30pm, frequently staying later. He often thinks that if only other people felt the same as him, and worked as hard, the company would be moving into a leading position in the market place.

Having reviewed the figures for the year to date, Douglas is disappointed. Despite being up 20% on last year the business is still trailing behind its two main industry rivals. Douglas has been doing all he can to get his staff to understand that they must contribute more if *Guardian Angel* is to become the market leader.

To help him do this, and to get a better perspective of what is happening throughout the company, Douglas has selected a range of people to talk to. People from different departments and different levels have been included (using the traditional language of organisations, in which some people are at the 'top' of the company and others are at the 'bottom'). As yet, nothing has really surprised him. Everyone he has seen so far agrees that the company could do better, and still no one has come up with anything particularly useful or new that would help take the company forward.

As Douglas pondered once again on this conundrum, a knock came at the door. Douglas realised that he had been sitting staring absent-mindedly out of the window for some time. Looking up he saw a tall, slim, blonde young woman standing in the open doorway. He wondered how long she had been waiting there, and what she had been thinking as she watched the Chief Executive gazing out of the window. And just how had she got past Bett?

Getting past Douglas's long-serving personal assistant, who was known in the company by her nickname 'Head of the Praetorian Guard', was quite a feat. The young woman could see Douglas's puzzlement and slight embarrassment. "I think Bett must have slipped out for a few moments," she said. "So I took the opportunity to pop in and say hello."

Douglas wondered what on earth this young employee thought she was doing "popping in" to see the Chief Executive. Doesn't she know I have every minute of every day accounted for?

"I have some insights that I thought you would be interested in," continued the woman. "But firstly let me introduce myself. My name is Lise, and I've been working in the company for two years in the Internal Communications section of the Marketing department."

"So what?" Douglas muttered to himself. Then he thought, if she can get this far and has the courage to suggest she can help in some way, maybe I should hear her out. "Sit down then, Lise, and tell me more," he said.

"I believe that you're currently confused about what else you can do to take *Guardian Angel* to its rightful place as market leader," said Lise.

Douglas opened his mouth, but nothing came out. How the hell did she know that?

"If I were to tell you that I could begin to open up your understanding of how to achieve your goal, would you be interested?" Lise asked.

Douglas once again did a convincing impression of a goldfish before managing to answer, in a barely audible voice. "Well, yes, of course I'd be interested. But I don't really see how you can."

"You've tried everything else," Lise replied, putting the emphasis on 'tried'. She knew that he had, as yet, only just scratched the surface. Douglas noted that she used 'everything' as a means of slightly dramatising the issue, perhaps hoping to persuade him to listen. "I can guarantee you insights which, when followed through, will change not only the way you think, but also the way this company works," Lise continued. "What's more, they'll take you to the number one position that you desire. No need to decide now. Have a think about what I've said and let me know."

What was there to think about? Douglas once again indulged himself with his vision of *Guardian Angel* leading the field. When he looked up again, he saw that Lise had gone. "Hey! Hold on a minute," shouted Douglas as he ran to the door.

"Yes?" said Bett curtly, from the outer office.

"Lise – where did she go?" Douglas asked.

"Lise who?" Bett replied.

"The young woman who just left my office."

For a moment Bett wondered if her leader was having a bad day, and then decided not to pursue a conversation about someone who, as far as she was concerned, didn't exist. "The... young woman must have slipped past while I was working on these letters, Mr Murray. Do you wish me to trace her for you?"

"No, no. It's okay," Douglas responded. He thought it better if he did the tracing, just in case Lise had only been a figment of his imagination. But unless he was going insane, he was certain she had been real.

Back in his office, Douglas decided to e-mail Lise to arrange a time to continue their discussion. He paused for a moment: the little episode with Lise would make interesting reading, he thought, if he ever decided to write his memoirs. She would make a delightful little cameo.

Chapter Two

An Awakening

*"Slowly but surely I began to realise that the whole
question of awakening is infinite in its subtlety and
complexity"*

Andrew Cohen

SIX O'CLOCK ALREADY. ANOTHER DAY OF MEETINGS WITH
little to show for it, Douglas thought. And a pile of
work still to be completed before finishing for the
day.

The meetings were essential to ensure that
Douglas's senior managers knew what was going on,
and to give them an opportunity to contribute their
ideas for the future. Douglas encouraged his senior
team to follow the same pattern with their staff, and
similarly the other teams throughout the company.
But he suspected that, at grassroots level, people were
probably only interested in doing their job in return
for a salary. Seldom, if ever, did they contribute anything new of note. For that matter, Douglas mused,
neither do most of my team; the majority of development ideas have come from me.

Since his meeting with Lise the previous morning,
Douglas had found it difficult to focus on his heavy

work schedule in his usual disciplined way. Every so often he found his mind wandering back to his encounter – his almost mystical meeting – with Lise. He had some unanswered questions: the main one being, how could Lise have known that he was confused about how to take the business forward? Douglas hadn't received a reply to the e-mail he'd sent Lise, and he began to wonder if he'd imagined the whole episode. He had a vague feeling that he'd read about something similar in one of his many books.

"You may be thinking that I'm just a figment of your imagination, but I feel pretty real myself," Lise announced as she entered Douglas's office after knocking gently on his door. "Thanks for your e-mail. E-mail is a great tool if used effectively and sparingly. Although I still believe that important issues are better dealt with face-to-face, don't you?"

Douglas was again taken aback by this young woman from the Marketing department. How old was she anyway? She wasn't even a junior manager, yet she had the nerve to walk unannounced into the Chief Executive's office and start discussing the pros and cons of e-mail. How did she know what he was thinking? Was he really that transparent?

"So, where do you want to start?" asked Lise.

"I'm not sure," replied Douglas. "You've caught me a bit on the hop, and I've a pile of work to get through tonight. I really would prefer if we scheduled a time to progress this investigation, or whatever it turns out to be."

"Your first lesson will be to learn that opportunities can't always be scheduled. When we stay conscious we can take advantage of opportunities as they occur. We'll have time to pursue this in more detail later – that's if you want to pursue it?"

Douglas started to wonder who was running this show. I'm supposed to be Chief Executive, not her, he thought. Douglas's ego was beginning to feel threatened, even although he was fascinated by what might lie ahead. Better re-assert my authority here and reschedule a meeting at a more appropriate time, he thought. "Look, Lise, I'm very keen to explore your insights into the company but, right now, I have to read these reports and send my comments to the senior team by tomorrow."

"What would happen if you didn't?" Lise asked, smiling. Her blue eyes were sparkling and she had a mischievous grin, which produced the faintest hint of dimples on her cheeks.

"They need my comments before they can finalise the reports," Douglas replied. As he said this, Douglas experienced a mildly uncomfortable feeling inside, as some of his readings on empowerment – readings about giving people responsibility and ownership – drifted back into his consciousness. That's all very well in theory, he thought, but in the real world I'm the one who carries the can for any mistakes.

"What's more important? The long-term success of the business or a set of reports which, after all, are only records of past events?" Lise asked.

Recognising that he was getting himself stuck in a corner, Douglas decided to compromise. "Okay, I'll give you an hour this evening. But in future we really must schedule our meetings."

Lise smiled to herself. "So, where do you want to start?" she asked, once again. "We can take it issue by issue if you like. Whatever suits you."

What confidence and poise in one so young, Douglas thought. "Well, what does irritate me is the apparent lack of motivation amongst many of our workforce. They have little drive and don't appear to have any real interest in the company and its success. To them it's just a job."

"Hmm. Let me show you something," said Lise, standing up and moving smoothly towards the door. She looked back to see Douglas still sitting firmly behind his desk. "Well, do you want to see?" she asked.

"Yes, of course. I just wasn't sure what you expected from me," Douglas replied. And following Lise through the door, he suddenly found himself standing in the dressing room of a football team. Douglas gasped in astonishment. "How did we get here?" he asked.

"I'll tell you later. Just watch and listen for a while."

The football manager was standing in front of his squad giving them a team talk, apparently at the start of a new season. Douglas wasn't quite sure what level the team played at, but he guessed it wasn't the Premier League. The manager had obviously modelled himself on the stereotype of the 'hard man' boss: his tone was harsh, aggressive and slightly patronising.

I don't fancy playing for him, Douglas thought to himself.

"Shhh," whispered Lise, as if she had read his mind. "Just listen."

"Can they see us?" Douglas asked, suddenly aware that they had appeared from nowhere.

"No, we're invisible to them," Lise replied.

The manager was getting into full flow. "You lads are the most talented players in our league. You are the most skilful and experienced. That's why we bought you," he said, looking and sounding rather self-satisfied. "Your task is to go out there each week and produce the goods – bring in the big 'Ws'."

"That's 'wins' to the uninitiated," Lise whispered to Douglas.

"There are a few conditions though," continued the manager. "Firstly, you won't know the score at the end of each game. Your job is to play; I'll worry about the score. Secondly, from time to time we'll move the goal posts during the game without telling you. Don't worry about this either; just adapt as best you can. They'll have been moved for a good strategic reason, so just carry on playing as if nothing has happened. Finally, we won't let you know where you are in the league until the end of the season, and even then we may decide not to tell you. Just keep in mind that your job is to go out each week and produce an outstanding performance."

A few players looked at each other with faint signs of disbelief on their faces.

"That's crazy!" Douglas spluttered, turning to Lise. "Who would want to play in that team?"

"Who indeed?" replied Lise, turning and walking back through the open door into Douglas's office. "Lesson one: few people, if any, can feel motivated if they are unaware of the effect they have on the outcome of any team or business, or on how successful they are over a period of time. They also find it difficult to commit fully to their work when things around them are changed without any reasonable explanation. Yet many people turn up at work each day and operate within these conditions. Is it any wonder most lack motivation?"

Douglas was deep in thought. Could this be happening at *Guardian Angel*? If so, how would he know about it?

"Why don't you ask them?" Lise responded.

Douglas looked up only to find that, frustratingly, Lise had once again quietly slipped out of the room – and without scheduling another meeting. As he pulled out his pile of reports, Douglas wondered if he was indeed going crazy.

Chapter Three

Contemplation

"That I feed the hungry, forgive an insult, and love my enemy – these are great virtues.   But what if I should discover that the poorest of the beggars and most impudent of offenders are all within me, and that I stand in need of the alms of my own kindness; that I myself am the enemy who must be loved, what then?"

C.G. Jung

DOUGLAS STROLLED ALONG HIS FAVOURITE WALK WITH his faithful Labrador, Tara. This was a good time to think, and he loved his walks in springtime the most. It was early May, the spring flowers had just begun to bud after the long winter and the blossom on the cherry trees was magnificent.

Douglas lived out of town, just on the edge of the countryside. His house was of red brick with some external beams showing, and had been built 120 years ago by one of the wealthy new business owners of the time. It stood in one and a half acres of mixed garden, with well-established trees and wild flowers at the back and a more formal garden closer to the house. At the side, within easy reach of the kitchen, Douglas's wife Pat kept a small herb and vegetable garden.

It's a pity I don't get the chance to spend as much time here as I'd like, Douglas thought, not for the first time. He stepped through the wooden gate at the bottom of the garden and onto the path towards the stream which bordered most of his daily walk.

Douglas had worked on at the office for an hour or so but had decided to come home earlier than his normal time of around 8pm. He felt he needed some time to think, and he was keen to update Pat on his first session with Lise.

Douglas had known Pat for 26 years. They had met at university; at 21, Douglas was entering his final year of his accountancy degree and at 18, Pat was just starting her degree in anthropology. They had been together ever since, except for one year when Pat went to Africa to work with Voluntary Services Overseas. Douglas and Pat married on her return. This summer they will celebrate their 22nd wedding anniversary.

They had wanted a family but it hadn't been possible and neither Douglas nor Pat had wanted to adopt. It had put some pressure on their marriage for a time, but they had come through it and all was well on that front. Thank goodness, Douglas thought. Pat was his best friend as well as his wife, although she had often jokingly complained that Douglas was a bigamist, married not only to her but also to *Guardian Angel*.

Pat has worked for various organisations. Strangely, after studying anthropology, her first job was as a marketing assistant in a publishing company. But Pat didn't enjoy her job and after a year moved to a charity to work as a research assistant. Over a period of time, Pat then developed her ability to raise funds through sponsorships and other relationships between charities and businesses. She now works part-time as a fundraising consultant for two major charities.

At 43, Pat is still very fit. She has always led an active life and complains that Douglas doesn't look after himself as well as he should. He had been a pretty good sportsman in his time, winning a cross-country running blue and playing off a five handicap at golf. Both these sporting achievements are now distant memories for him. Douglas now works out in the gym only occasionally, and plays golf a few times a year – badly by his standards, but quite acceptably by most others'.

But Douglas did enjoy the walks, which helped him think through the many complex issues he has to deal with at *Guardian Angel*. Putting aside his amazing experience with Lise for a moment, Douglas's mind turned to thoughts of the potential take-over of the company by one of the major banks. He'd been in discussions for almost a year, firstly with two possible suitors and latterly with the most likely buyer. This is what he had worked so hard for, for so long. If and when the take-over went through, Douglas would receive a considerable pay rise, some generous share options and a very sizeable pension to come. Early retirement, a few non-executive posts in the City and a holiday retreat in the South of France were all part of his dream.

But there were still some doubts in his mind about giving up what he saw as his baby. Under his leadership, *Guardian Angel* had grown consistently and, over the past three years, had trebled the funds under management. But Douglas had also dreamed of creating a company in which the people were as highly motivated and enthusiastic about the business as he was. He quite obviously had not succeeded in making this dream a reality, and his first awakening with Lise had started him thinking again about how this could be achieved.

The football team scenario had certainly hit home. Douglas wondered what it would feel like to work each day not knowing how his input affected the progress of the business, either directly or indirectly. And he wondered how many people really knew how the company was doing and whether they really cared. Douglas suspected that he had been right in believing that all that most people wanted was a safe job that gave them a little left over for a few luxuries, including their holidays. Douglas shook his head as he remembered his own childhood and how holidays were occasional days away at the seaside. He had enjoyed his upbringing but his family had never had that much money, and most of what they had was spent on necessities. How life and expectations have changed. The overall level of material wealth has increased dramatically over Douglas's lifetime, with a proportional decrease in satisfaction in many cases. Even the most poorly paid of his people would be able to afford a great deal more than his own family when he had been a child. So why aren't they motivated and satisfied? Douglas's last question was spoken aloud and directed at Tara, who was enjoying her favourite smells and familiar places.

Tara turned around and looked at Douglas as she heard the questioning tone in his voice. She knows how to be happy, Douglas laughed to himself. Tara skipped forward, as if pleased that her master seemed happy with her. She picked up a stick and came bounding over with it, tail wagging and looking up at Douglas with anticipation of even more fun.

What a great leveller dogs were, Douglas thought. No matter how tough the day had been, she's always delighted to see me and she lifts my spirit with her sparkle.

They were almost back at the house. "Where did you get to?" asked Pat, who was collecting some herbs from her garden.

"Didn't realise the time, darling. I was deep in thought. Still mulling over the take-over and fascinated by my session with Lise today."

"Oh, the blonde and beautiful mystery woman?" Pat laughed. She trusted Douglas implicitly and knew that he would keep this interesting new relationship very much on a business footing.

"You know, she took me straight out of my office and into a football team's dressing room today."

Pat looked at Douglas with a quizzical and disbelieving expression. Yet she knew he was the sanest of individuals, not prone to hallucinating.

"Go on," said Pat. She thought it best to allow Douglas the chance to explain more fully.

"She appears to have magical... No, let me rephrase that. She has magical – possibly mystical – powers, including being able to read my thoughts."

"Well, I've been doing that for years!" exclaimed Pat. And they both burst into laughter.

"No, really. Lise can specifically read my every thought, and was able to create this scenario for me right outside my office, using a door which doesn't normally exist," continued Douglas.

"And was the scenario useful?"

"It has definitely raised a few questions about how we could create a more motivating environment in the business. Lise showed me a football team talk where the manager told his players that he expected them to be the best in the league. Yet he told them that they wouldn't be told the score in games, they would have the goal posts moved regularly without being told and they would not be informed about their position in the league during the season."

"Hold me back!" Pat joked. "Pretty de-motivating then?"

"Most definitely. The depressing thing is, Lise was inferring that that is what the reality is for most people in *Guardian Angel*. They turn up for work and are expected to perform to high standards, but, according to Lise, are given little or no feedback on how they are doing. Their 'goal posts' are moved frequently without any explanation and they don't really know how we compare with our competitors."

"Don't think I'd get out of bed in the morning for that." Pat shook her head.

"I'm not totally convinced about her conclusions. My experience is that most people see their jobs as a necessity, to pay their bills and to be able to live reasonably well. However, my first experiences with Lise have persuaded me to put aside the next three days to investigate the insights she may be able to give me."

Douglas wasn't sure how Pat would take this. She looked at him with a mixture of affection and astonishment.

"Three days! That's some commitment for you. You must be impressed with her. I'll have to have a word with Lise to discover her secret," Pat joked.

"I just have this intuitive feeling that I must do this. I can't explain why. Perhaps it's all the turmoil I'm experiencing at the moment, wondering whether selling *Guardian Angel* is the right thing to do. I know I'm not the only one who will make the final decision.

Besides my fellow Board Directors, our members have to vote for it too. But I have a key influence in it."

"*The* key influence," Pat interjected.

"Perhaps," Douglas replied. "But I have this feeling that I'm giving up on something, that we could make *Guardian Angel* so much more. So I see this opportunity to spend time with Lise as a wonderful chance to review where I am, and what I really want."

"She sounds like a fascinating person, so I'm not surprised that you want to continue your work with her." Pat linked her arm through Douglas's. "Let's go inside and have dinner." They turned to walk towards the house, and Tara took this as her signal to stir herself from her reverie on the grass and trot beside them. The possibility of more food was always at the forefront of her mind.

* * * *

"Shoot, you idiot!" The coach was on the touchline, screaming at his team. Douglas was sitting in the stand wondering how the hell the player could possibly shoot. The goalposts seemed to disappear as he lined up his shot. By the time they reappeared, a defender from the opposition had taken possession of the ball.

"Get wide! Get wide!" The coach was going crazy.

"What's the score?" asked someone who had sat down next to Douglas.

"Don't know. I've just arrived," Douglas replied, shrugging his shoulders.

"How many times have I told you – stay deep! You're a bunch of ******* useless ********." The coach's voice could be heard throughout the ground.

The coach's attitude was starting to annoy

Douglas. That's no way to get players to perform, he thought. Douglas realised he hadn't been to see a match for some time, and he wasn't sure he'd come back again in a hurry.

Douglas noticed that the ground was a shambles, with only a few spectators scattered around it. Whatever possessed me to come here? The players looked fed up, and had started shouting and gesticulating at the coach.

"Leave them alone!" Douglas had started shouting at the coach without even realising.

"Quite right!" Douglas's neighbour agreed with his sentiments.

"Let them play their own game, you idiot!" Douglas was getting carried away. He was standing up now and pointing his finger, which seemed for a moment to get longer, at the coach.

"Who do you think you are?" asked the coach, turning to Douglas.

"Oh my God, it's me!" Douglas exclaimed. And at that moment he felt an elbow in his side.

"Having a bad dream, darling?" Pat whispered.

Douglas rolled over onto his back and took a deep breath.

"An interesting one," he replied, smiling.

Chapter Four

Mapping the Journey

*"Afoot and light-hearted I take to the open road, healthy,
free, the world before me. The long grown path leading
wherever I choose."*

Walt Whitman

D RIVING TO WORK THE NEXT MORNING, DOUGLAS WAS
still in a state of shock over his experience the
day before. How could he have walked out of his
office and into a football team's dressing room to listen to a team talk? It was just not possible, yet it had
happened.

Douglas remembered that he hadn't completely
finished reading his managers' reports. He wondered
how his senior team would react if he told them that
from now on they would finalise the reports themselves and he would only read through them for
information. Would they cope? Would I cope?
Douglas wondered which was more important. I
think I understand what empowerment is, yet I'm not
sure if I'm really making it work. Could I be part of
preventing the people at *Guardian Angel* from being
empowered? Not likely! Douglas dismissed the possibility of such a thing.

Rescheduling a number of meetings and appointments over the next three days gave Douglas the chance to spend some more time with Lise discussing her insights. One of the things he intended to do was spend time talking to front-. liners to find out about their motivation, or, as he saw it, their lack of it. Douglas also wanted to investigate why empowerment wasn't working and how he could get it to work. That would do for starters. Douglas had read so many books that he felt he could almost write, or even feature in one, himself.

Before Bett came in, Douglas e-mailed his colleagues to rearrange his various appointments and meetings, then he mapped out his reorganised schedule.

"You intend to spend three days with this young woman from Marketing?" Bett asked, with a faint hint of scorn in her voice. She had always prided herself on her loyalty to Mr Murray (she had never quite been able to get the hang of calling him Douglas – except at Christmas parties – although he had told her he preferred this). One of the 'old school' of PAs, Bett is in her mid-fifties, a widow of ten years with adult children. A brunette with streaks of grey running through her well-kept, short hair, she always looks in control. Bett is well organised and on top of her job, always keeping up-to-date with new technology and using it to good effect. In turn, Bett's assistance helps keep Douglas well organised and allows him to juggle his considerable workload. She is glad they share the need to be organised and in control. It was because of this that Douglas's sudden desire to abandon three days of meetings, appointments and other commitments to spend time with a front-line employee completely baffled her.

Sensing her disapproval, Douglas retired to his

office. He wanted to check his e-mail to see if Lise had responded to his request to meet in his office at 9am. As he logged on, Douglas noticed that over 60 messages awaited him. Remembering Lise's advice regarding the use of e-mail, Douglas sifted through the messages to find the important one. Lise would be with him at 9.15 as she had one or two loose ends to tie up before joining him.

"Well, this is a surprise!" It seemed as if Lise had just floated into the room and sat down. "Three days to explore my insights into the company. It'll be a start," she laughed. Lise noticed Douglas wasn't finding it too amusing – he was looking rather tense and impatient. "Don't be nervous," she said sympathetically. "This will be the journey of a lifetime. Just imagine you're a character in a book and that I'm writing the book. Relax and enjoy the opportunity to see behind the masks and armour that people wear. We'll look behind the hidden agendas, the politicking and, of course, the games-playing. You may be disappointed when you experience the lack of authenticity of some of the behaviours you'll see. You will also rejoice in the real potential of your self, your people and your company. When we take the lid off, you'll be amazed at the potential lying hidden beneath the surface. Potential to make the company more successful, financially and in every other way. The potential to create a place where people want to be; a place which buzzes with productive energy and intent; a place where there is a connection between people in everything they do, not only internally, but with our customers, suppliers and communities at large. What many people forget is the impact that their business, and the way it is run, has on society as a whole. They need to recognise that the old paradigms of organisations no longer serve us well, if indeed they ever did. What we need are new paradigms, new models, and new leaders. This is your opportunity to take the lead and change business life for the better. Empowerment is something you've been struggling with of late. Would this be an appropriate place to begin?"

Douglas still didn't feel too comfortable. He was wondering if he'd made a mistake. What would he find out about the company? More importantly, perhaps, what would he find out about himself? Douglas hadn't yet realised that being uncomfortable was essential to his growth as a person and that his discomfort should be welcomed as a companion on the journey of transformation. He was so used to avoiding these feelings, by 'getting on with it', that the concept of 'letting go' to explore himself and his company for three days was rather frightening. But the things Lise had just said inspired him to take that step. What Douglas wasn't sure about was his ability to be truly different, to think and act differently, to shake off the traditional values and beliefs about how senior executives and company leaders should be. He had learned these values and beliefs the hard way, having worked his way up through the ranks from trainee chartered accountant to Chief Executive.

These ways had worked in the past, so why change? 'If it ain't broke, don't fix it' was a phrase imported from across the Atlantic which was wheeled out by colleagues whenever change was in the air. He could recall, however, listening to Frank Merlotti the CEO of Steelcase who changed the phrase to 'If it ain't broke, break it'. It was his intuitive feeling that something different was required that had started this process of introspection.

Wasn't it strange, fortuitous even, that Lise had turned up just as he'd been wondering how the company could make the progress he desired? Although Lise had yet to prove that she would be able to deliver the insights required, Douglas's sneak preview of the football team had been illuminating and had already set his mind to work on changes he'd like to make.

"Yes, it's a pretty controversial issue and one which we've been grappling with for some time. Empowerment it is then…"

Chapter Five

Who's Responsible?

"To be yourself in a world which does its best to make you someone else means fighting the hardest battle that any human being can fight, and never stop fighting."
C.C. Cummings

"HAVE YOU EVER BEEN LATE IN LEAVING TO DRIVE somewhere for an appointment?" Lisa asked

"Yes," replied Douglas, knowing only too well that this was a pretty normal occurrence for him. But he wondered what it had to do with empowerment.

"Have you noticed that when you do this, there are idiots out there," Lise continued, pointing outside, "who have the audacity to drive at 30 miles an hour in a 30 miles per hour zone?"

"Yeah. It feels as if I could walk faster sometimes," said Douglas.

"And have you also noticed that every light turns to red as you approach it? You know that if you were a traffic engineer you'd make sure that when you went through the first light at green, every other set would be at green when you got to them. Also, when you drive on country roads the farmers' Mafia goes to work and produces a tractor just when you've hit

25

double bends for three miles."

"Exactly!" Douglas agreed, laughing at the thought.

"So when we eventually arrive late for the appointment, we say something like, 'Sorry I'm late – it was the traffic' and this is received with nodding heads all round," Lise continued. "Wouldn't it be more authentic to say 'I'm terribly sorry I'm late, I just can't get my act together enough to leave on time for appointments'. Too risky perhaps, though in the long-term it would be more productive. Most people are unaware that they run their own 'business'."

Douglas was looking puzzled again. "I don't quite follow you," he said.

"Okay. Let me ask you, whose business is your life?"

"My own, of course," Douglas almost snapped back, as yet unaware of where this line of discussion was going.

"Exactly!" Lise was smiling broadly.

Douglas noticed how perfect her teeth were: they were almost sparkling.

"This, of course, is the same for everyone." Lise emphasised the 'of course' to match Douglas's previous response. "Since your life is your own, and if your life is your business, then it follows that we are all running our own 'business'. It's just that most people have never truly awakened to this fact, and live their lives in the mistaken belief that someone else should be responsible for them. Empowerment is not a management technique, nor an organisational initiative; it is a state of mind. This is the major mistake people make when they attempt to 'introduce' empowerment. True empowerment comes when people look to themselves for the answers they need, when they realise there are choices in the way they perceive themselves, the world and the circumstances they are in, that how they feel is their own responsibility. Only then can they begin to act differently in what we sometimes call 'the real world'. Does that make sense?"

"Yes, it does. What you're saying is that people usually find someone, or something, to blame when things go wrong. Like when we're late we blame the traffic?"

"Spot on," said Lise. "Next time you're stuck in traffic, just say gently to yourself, 'I am responsible'."

"That could frustrate me even more," Douglas replied. "I'm pretty good at beating myself up as it is without adding this."

"I'm not suggesting you beat yourself up, rather that you release yourself from blame and open up to find solutions. Do you play golf?" Lise asked Douglas.

"When I get the time," he responded.

"Have you ever stood over a four-foot putt and said to yourself, 'I could miss this?'"

"Yes, often." Douglas smiled.

"And what happened?"

"I missed it, of course."

"Isn't it interesting that we can easily achieve an outcome like that, and then follow it up with a comment like 'I knew I was going to do that!' It's how we unconsciously programme ourselves. Every time we self-dialogue, or speak to others for that matter, our unconscious mind – also known as our subconscious mind – processes the meaning of what we say and goes to work to provide us with the outcomes we've programmed. So, when we say to ourselves, 'I am responsible', what do you reckon our unconscious mind looks for?"

"Solutions, of course!" Douglas again chose to use 'of course' to emphasise his speed of uptake and his frustration that this all seemed too simple.

"This, then, is the hub of empowerment, or whatever you like to call it." Lise was enthusing on this line of thought. "When people, ourselves included, take full responsibility for circumstances, as they are in our lives, we can then begin to find the solutions for the things which aren't working." This was an 'Ah!' moment, thought Lise, but she would enlighten Douglas on these later. "Most people, unfortunately are addicted to their T.T.I.s," continued Lise.

"Less of the jargon please, Lise. Keep it simple!"

Interesting, thought Lise. Earlier he was frustrated because it seemed too easy, but now he is asking me to keep it simple.

"The T.T.I.s are our 'theys', 'thems' and 'its'," Lise explained. "We'll have a chance shortly to listen to how people use them in their everyday lives. We've already had one example: when we're late for an appointment, we say, 'It was the traffic'. People frequently use their T.T.I.s to avoid taking responsibility for their own 'business'. I wonder, Douglas, if you've ever used a 'they' or 'them' when something didn't work successfully?" This was the first time Lise had referred to Douglas by his Christian name and she could see that he stiffened a little as she said it.

"What do you mean?" Douglas was smarting a bit.

"Well, take empowerment, for example. It could be that you've said something like, 'We've done all these things for 'them' and 'they' still don't respond."

"I suppose I have felt those sentiments in the past. Whether or not I used those exact words I couldn't be sure." Douglas was rather grudging in agreeing that he used this type of language. He was certainly aware that he'd felt very frustrated at times, especially when people wouldn't contribute above and beyond what they were paid to do.

"Would you like to see and hear for yourself?" Lise asked Douglas.

"What do you mean?" Douglas had a feeling that he was in for another peculiar experience.

"How would you like to be a fly on the wall whilst some of your people demonstrate empowerment in the company?"

"You mean sit in on a meeting?"

"Sort of, except that they won't know we're there." Lise grinned.

Having witnessed the football team the previous day, Douglas was beginning to believe anything could happen.

"There's a meeting of middle managers in progress on the second floor if you'd like to join them," said Lise.

They headed out of Douglas's seventh floor office and took the lift to the second floor. He had never noticed this particular lift before. It was very swift and extremely quiet – the journey from seventh to second floor was over in a flash. As they came out of the lift Douglas smiled and nodded to the people waiting for another lift. He thought it strange that they looked straight through him. At least that's how it felt.

"You're right," observed Lise. "They can't see you."

"You mean we've become invisible again?" What a weird feeling, thought Douglas.

"In here," directed Lise, walking through the door into a meeting room. She waved Douglas through and he sat down beside her at the back of the room.

Wow, what an opportunity, thought Douglas. Yet, at the back of his mind, he was nervous of what he might see and hear.

"So, Ellie, if this idea of yours will make a minimum of 10% savings on current costs and open up an opportunity to significantly increase sales, why don't you take it upstairs to your boss?" asked Mike Duncan, the manager responsible for new product marketing.

"It cuts across their new strategy, so they'd never buy it," replied Ellie James, the junior member of this marketing development group, with a weary look on her face. "And what's the point in rocking the boat? If I go against their strategy it'll make me look bad for future promotion. They're not really interested in what we've got to say. They just want to make sure they please 'Deadly Doug'."

"That's you," Lise whispered to Douglas.

Why she whispered she wasn't quite sure. Probably just to add to the drama for Douglas.

'Deadly Doug' – Douglas wondered where that had come from. But what was really disturbing was what he had just heard – a manager in *Guardian Angel* had an idea which could save the company money and increase sales, yet she wasn't prepared to take it forward. He'd soon sort this out, he thought. He'd have it out with those responsible for stifling innovation.

"Calm down and listen." Lise had noticed Douglas's agitation.

"All we hear round here just now is that we're now an empowered organisation. I'm not sure I know what that means," continued Ellie. "But I don't see much evidence of it in my department."

Bill Dow, the assistant manager of the New Product Marketing division, who was chairing the meeting, was clearly becoming impatient at this line of discussion. "I think we should move on to look at our current sales performance for this quarter," he said. "Although we are only a little behind our target, we are well behind our key competitors." Needless to say, Bill didn't look too happy about the situation.

"The targets are set too high in the first place," Ann Edwards retorted. "They are totally unrealistic. Just look at the market right now. We have to contend with increased competition. Some of our competitors are even prepared to 'give away' their products simply to get new business. The economy isn't helping us, as the pound is too strong at the moment. And they won't give us the go-ahead to recruit new people. How we are expected to achieve our targets under these conditions I don't know."

May Davidson, a newcomer to the company, was feeling increasingly uncomfortable. She couldn't understand why Ellie wouldn't take her idea forward, and she identified as excuses all the reasons Ann had given for not reaching her targets. Why were they not looking for solutions? Why not put our energy into achieving the set targets?

"Why doesn't May speak up?" Douglas asked Lise in a 'loud' whisper. As he spoke he realised he was now tuning in to people's thoughts.

"It's a common occurrence," Lise replied. "Many people don't have the confidence and self-belief to speak their mind, to truly say what they think and feel. That's why so many people get frustrated with the meetings they attend and say things like, 'we have all these meetings and never really get anywhere'. That's because they never really meet each other in the true sense of the word. They spend a lot of time saying, or not saying, things to suit the other people involved and, in particular, the most senior people present. Seen enough for now?" Lise asked Douglas. "We can look in on more later."

Douglas and Lise left the room as they had entered it and travelled swiftly back to the seventh floor.

"Where do we start?" Douglas groaned, sinking into his leather seat.

Chapter Six

Getting Conscious

"Everyone wants to be comfortable – but that is the addiction which stops any creative growth."

Swami Rudrananda (Rudi)

"LISE, I CAN'T BELIEVE THAT PEOPLE FEEL UNABLE TO present their ideas to their manager, especially ideas that will benefit the company." Douglas was astonished at what he had just heard and seen in his own company, especially from his managers.

"Is this endemic in the business? How do these attitudes take root? Can they be changed? How do we start?" Douglas asked Lise.

"Which question shall I answer first?" Lise was smiling again, which irritated Douglas, as he didn't see much to smile about. "I hate to depress you further," Lise continued swiftly, giving Douglas no time to reply to her own question. "What you saw was only the tip of the iceberg. The exciting point is that it is possible to change, once we awaken to the need to change and genuinely want to. What we have to understand is that this process is not often easy. In a sense, the easiest change is that which is forced upon us, as in the case of someone who has been made redundant. It is not unusual for them to seize this opportunity and use their cash settlement to establish their own business, suddenly realising that they've had this dormant ambition all along."

"In more dramatic cases," Lise continued, "some people have admitted that they only really started living – actually being who they wanted to be, and doing the things they wanted to do – when they were told that they had a limited amount of time left to live. Once we have become 'conditioned' to our world it's hard for most of us to change. If confronted with an opportunity to do things differently, people will say, 'Why bother? Nothing's going to change anyway'. Am I going on a bit?"

"No, no. I'm taking it in. I can see why these people find it hard to change."

"May I suggest that this includes yourself," Lise said, gently. She wanted to take Douglas along with her rather than antagonise him. "Can I give you a practical example?" Douglas nodded a little apprehensively. "It won't hurt!" Lise said, smiling broadly once again. "I'd like to use an everyday activity as the example so that it can act as a trigger to stay conscious in other contexts. Allow me to introduce you to a more effective way of sitting on your chair. Are you game?"

Douglas nodded, although he wondered why the heck she was doing this when there were so many other more important issues to deal with.

"Why don't you voice your concerns, Douglas? Tell me how you're feeling."

There she goes, reading my mind again, he thought.

"It didn't seem important to voice them," Douglas responded. "I was willing to go along with what you were saying, although I wasn't convinced of its relevance."

"Can you see any similarities between this example and what you saw in the meeting a short while ago?" Lise asked.

"Hmmm, yes. But that's natural isn't it?" Douglas responded.

"More 'common' than 'natural'. As you've seen, people learn not to voice their thoughts and feelings in organisations and as a result never really contribute their true potential." Lise paused to allow Douglas to take in the full significance of this and awaken to his own conditioning and need to change.

"Back to sitting," she continued. "Start by pushing your bottom into the base of the seat so that your back is supported by your sacrum, the large bone at the base of your back. Okay so far?"

Douglas nodded, directing his full attention to the task at hand and beginning to enjoy the experience.

"Now, uncross your legs and put your feet flat on the ground and your hands comfortably on your thighs. Note also, if you can, that your head is sitting on top of your shoulders, neither drawn back nor leaning forward or to one side. Good. That looks really good." Lise managed to prompt a little smile from Douglas who was beginning to realise how often he resisted new ideas or approaches that he hadn't thought of himself.

"Now let me give you some information about this 'new' sitting position." Lise warmed easily to her task. "By sitting this way more frequently you will open up your energy centres, improve your circulation – and thereby increase the amount of oxygen getting to your brain – plus you will reduce the potential for the head, neck and back aches, etc. which we often blame on old age. All very productive information, don't you think?"

"Yes, definitely," Douglas replied, looking as if he was desperate to get back to his 'normal' sitting position.

"Are you comfortable sitting like that?" Lise continued.

"Definitely not!" Douglas was sure about that.

"Relax then, and sit whichever way you wish."

Douglas breathed a sigh of relief and shifted his weight to a more side-on angle, sliding slightly forward as he crossed one leg over the other. "That's better!" he said.

"Do you notice, Douglas, that despite the fact that you agreed that the information I just gave you was highly productive, you chose not to act on it when given the choice. You reverted back to what felt more comfortable." At this point Lise stood up and walked – glided, Douglas thought – to the flipchart that stood in the corner of the room and wrote:

COMFORTABLE

$\neq$

PRODUCTIVE

"So you can see that what feels comfortable isn't necessarily productive for us."

"Turning that on its head," Douglas took over enthusiastically, "becoming more productive will mean having to experience a period of being uncomfortable?"

"Yes." Lise confirmed his conclusion. "At least for a period of time, before the new behaviour becomes part of you. This is the reason why people find it a real challenge to put into practice what they learn from traditional training programmes. People really do need to be supported through the process of 'real change'."

Douglas's mind ran back to all the books he'd read, the seminars he had attended and presentations he'd given on 'change'. He began to realise that although he knew and understood that the changes presented were productive, he himself had probably failed to embrace those changes as effectively as he could have done.

"People tend to misunderstand how challenging real change can be. And when we look at the world in general, what goes by the name of 'change' seems more often than not to be 'more of the same'."

"What do you mean?" It seemed to ring some bells for him, but Douglas wasn't entirely sure that he had grasped Lise's point.

"Well, if you take the issues that are most politically-sensitive in our country, like health, crime and transport, there has been little real change in any of them."

"Oh, come on." Douglas resisted. "The technological advances have been immense over the past ten or twenty years. You can't argue with the facts."

"No, it's certainly true that there have been huge advances in technology," conceded Lise. "But have they significantly or fundamentally changed what has happened in these areas? For example, despite the fact that we have had monumental advances in technology, hospital waiting lists continue to grow, crime figures are on the increase and our roads are grinding to a halt. And yet what we seem to want in all of these cases is 'more of the same' – more hospitals, more police and prisons and more roads or more lanes on motorways."

Lise paused for a moment to catch her breath, and to give Douglas a chance to respond.

"So, what would your answer be?" Douglas's response sounded a little interrogative.

"Take health for example. We don't really have a National Health Service, we have a 'National Ill Service', since the vast majority of the budget is spent on curing illnesses with very little spent on prevention. Imagine if a political party claimed that it would REDUCE the number of hospitals by 20% over a ten-year period – would that be a vote-puller?"

"Not especially." Douglas smiled. "Although it may depend on the ideas behind it, and how they were presented."

"Agreed," Lise continued. "It's the same in businesses. 'If in doubt, frighten people' seems to be the answer. Frighten people about losing their job, closing the business, and so on. And, when businesses are faced with a downturn in the economy, have you noticed how unimaginative they are?"

"What do you mean?" Douglas looked quite indignant at this since Lise was probably including him in this claim.

"Generally, they resort to 'more of the same' – to cost-cutting, reduction in their workforce, reduced marketing and training, etc."

Douglas couldn't argue that this resembled *Guardian Angel*'s own response to downturns in the past.

"So what's the answer then?"

"I don't think there is a single answer," Lise replied. "What I do believe is that no matter the circumstances we find ourselves in, there will be opportunities available if we take the time to look. If we can accept that everything happens for a reason, we can begin to search out the reasons, and the opportunities."

Douglas was beginning to show signs of his well-developed scepticism for all things non-rational. Lise sensed this, and decided it was almost time to come back to her original point on personal change. But first, just one more observation on the lack of change within organisations.

"Take a look at this." Lise jumped back up to the flipchart and wrote down the following words:

COMPANY
DIVISION
UNIT
STAFF
LINE OF COMMAND
RANK AND FILE

"You probably have all of these within your business. For example, you are a company?" Lise asked, smiling.

Douglas nodded in agreement, already beginning to get the point.

"You have divisions and units, you refer to people as staff, and so on?"

Douglas nodded again

"And you obviously recognise these as a collection of terms from another type of organisation, yes?"

"All military terms. Interesting when they're put together like that. Quite amazing."

"Not so amazing, because your own knowledge of organisations means you know that when management theory was invented in the 19th century, the military was one of only two organisations that the pioneers had as a model."

"The other being the Church," Douglas added.

"Isn't it amazing, then, that in this post-industrial, high-tech, knowledge age our major organisations still use the military language that they borrowed in the 19th century?"

"It is a bit strange when you look at it like that."

Lise spotted a good opportunity to bring the discussion back to change at a more personal level. "Getting back to our discussion on personal change, most people will avoid the things which make them uncomfortable, unless – and this again is crucial – they place a very high level of importance on them or have a high degree of support. Preferably both. Like learning to drive a car – almost everyone finds their first few lessons uncomfortable but because they WANT to drive, they stick with it. So to stimulate people to truly change they must want to do things differently."

Douglas was listening intently. "So how do I get people to WANT to change and use more of their potential?" he asked, desperate for the answer, the 'key'. What is the key to transforming the company and putting it at the top of the league? (Nice analogy, he thought to himself, remembering the football team scenario he had witnessed a couple of days previously.)

"The starting point for any leader who wants to change their team or their company's behaviour is their self. The clearest and most significant signal they can give is to change their own behaviour," Lise explained.

"But I've spent hours telling my managers what I want and how I want to see the company develop, and nothing significant has every really happened."

"Have you ever considered what you could DO differently yourself that would be a signal to everyone that the company is changing? Let me show you a couple of film clips. Remember this one?" Lise asked Douglas.

Douglas turned to the screen at the far end of his room. A film of him speaking at the last annual conference flickered into life.

"We want this to be an open organisation with no barriers to progress, where everyone respects their colleagues no matter what job they do. We are all here to contribute and it is important we all feel empowered to play our part in making *Guardian Angel* the leading company in the field." Douglas rather liked that speech and felt that he had hit the perfect tone for the end of the conference. Everyone he'd spoken to had said how inspiring it had been.

"Now have a look at this," Lise said, pressing a few buttons on what looked like a mini computer.

"What a load of codswallop that was yesterday. Did you hear him, old 'Deadly Doug', going on about us being an open and empowered organisation?" Mike Duncan asked his assistant, Bill Dow. "In one breath he's saying that, then this morning he walked right past me as if I didn't exist. That was after parking his car in the senior managers' parking area and travelling up in their special lift. If I were running *Guardian Angel* as an open and empowered company, it would be first-come-first-served for the parking spaces. We've heard all this before. It won't change a thing, you know."

Douglas had changed colour several times whilst watching the second film clip. Lise switched the film off using her special gadget and sat back, watching him.

"If he doesn't like the way things are, why doesn't Mike do something about it instead of complaining?

If I sat around all day complaining the company would grind to a halt," said Douglas.

"You have a point," Lise conceded, "in that complaining gets us nowhere, and that Mike most probably could change things if he wanted to, or believed that you sincerely wanted those changes."

"Well of course I do. Hadn't I just told them so the previous day?" Douglas was getting rather annoyed.

"What you 'say' and what you 'do' differ at present. For any of us to change, we have to give up part of who we currently are. A clear tangible sign of this could be giving up reserved parking spaces for senior managers. Management, in effect, must give away a bit of their perceived status and a bit of their ego, both of which get in the way of creating the type of company you want. Acknowledging your colleagues is also of vital importance," suggested Lise.

"I had a lot on my mind that morning, I didn't even see Mike passing me. And I don't know what you mean when you say I have to give away a bit of my ego." Douglas was becoming increasingly defensive.

"This is your opportunity to sit back and look at how things are behind the scenes, if you like. Put yourself in Mike's shoes for a moment and ask yourself whether you've ever experienced similar emotions." Lise ignored Douglas's comment on his ego.

"Yes, I can see why he feels the way he does," Douglas said a little grudgingly. "And I'm beginning to realise what you mean by experiencing discomfort. I must admit to being uncomfortable about the possibility of giving up my reserved parking space and, more to the point, telling all those senior managers that they will be giving theirs up too. And I admit that I don't always feel comfortable speaking to people further down the organisation. I think it intimidates some of them."

"I'm glad you're beginning to experience the challenges of real change. We will come back to your final point and your comment on your ego later." Lise was keen to move on; she wanted to concentrate on further awakening Douglas to his own social conditioning and how this affects the way he thinks and acts. "Let's take another walk," Lise said, standing up and moving towards the door. She would return to the challenge of becoming conscious later.

Chapter Seven

The Well-Trodden Path

"I shall be telling this with a sigh
somewhere ages and ages hence:
two roads diverged in a wood,
and I took the one less travelled by,
and that made all the difference."

Robert Frost

STEPPING THROUGH THE DOORWAY, DOUGLAS ONCE again found himself transported, just as he had been when he and Lise had entered the football dressing room. This time Douglas found himself standing with Lise in a field on the edge of a dense wood. Just to their left was a well-trodden path leading through the trees and undergrowth. It was a mature wood, mainly deciduous with a scattering of evergreens and pretty dense undergrowth – very much a 'natural' wood, where little woodland management had taken place.

"Shall we take a stroll?" Lise asked, heading off towards the path without waiting for an answer. Douglas took a few quick steps to catch up with her. They reached the path together, walking side by side. The ground underfoot was dry and springy. Layers of bark and leaves had built up over time, making the path a pleasantly comfortable surface to walk on.

"Did you notice how easily we were drawn to the path?" asked Lise.

"What do you mean?" Douglas replied, not sure about what she was getting at.

"Well, because there was a well-trodden path available, we took it, didn't we?"

"Of course we did. Why shouldn't we?"

"I'm not saying we shouldn't. I'm asking if you were conscious of choosing the path, or whether you chose it because it was the easiest route through the wood?"

"We took it because it was there. It was the obvious thing to do. What else could we have done?" Douglas still couldn't see where this was going.

"If you were to return, would you take the path again?" Lise asked.

"Well, of course!"

"What would happen if we walked off the path and through the undergrowth?" continued Lise.

"We could get lost for a start, and it would probably be extremely uncomfortable." As Douglas uttered that last word, a look of realisation came over his face.

Another 'Ah!' moment, Lise thought. I must explain to Douglas about them soon, she reminded herself.

Warming to his discovery, Douglas said, "It would take us to places we couldn't possibly reach if we simply stayed on the well-trodden path." Douglas was now feeling pretty pleased with himself.

"Exactly." Lise was again smiling, her eyes sparkling as the sunlight streaked through between the trees. "And so it is with our thoughts and the actions we choose in life. It's easier simply to follow the 'well-trodden path' in our mind, rather than be conscious enough to notice that there are many other options. Can you see now why your people continue to do much as they've always done, rather than choose a new route?" Lise asked She noticed that Douglas had nodded his agreement, but continued without waiting for his reply. "As you saw in the meeting, people will take the 'safe' route, being afraid that to suggest or do something different would meet with disapproval. Can you imagine the potential that would be released when your people feel safe enough to 'step off the path' and explore the unexplored?"

"How do we create that culture?" Douglas recognised this as being the kind of empowered culture he was looking for. Suddenly, as if by magic, he realised that he probably had only thought that he wanted it, but had helped to keep things much as they always had been through his fear of mistakes. Douglas realised that he would have to be first to veer off the path, to accept responsibility for any mistakes along the way. He would have to demonstrate, through his own action, that he was willing to explore the unknown, take risks and, as a result, give permission to others to do the same.

"This is too easy," Douglas said, turning and smiling at Lise. "Let's head back across country." Douglas crunched through the undergrowth, bending down to avoid the low branches of a tree. Lise followed, her laughter resonating around the woodland.

The going was pretty hard at times, with difficult conditions underfoot. Neither Douglas nor Lise were quite sure they were heading in exactly the right direction but both were confident they'd reach their destination.

"Hey! Look at this!" In his enthusiasm, Douglas

had walked on ahead of Lise. He had come across a natural clearing, almost circular in shape, about ten metres across.

"Wow!" Lise was also impressed. "These flowers are beautiful." She bent down to get a better look at some delicate blue wild flowers.

The sun broke through the clouds at this point, sending shafts of glorious sunlight, filtered by the surrounding trees, into the clearing.

"What a gorgeous place," Lise said, sitting down on the mixture of grass and moss, "with comfortable seating provided, too." She smiled as she crossed her legs.

Douglas and Lise sat in silence for a couple of minutes, breathing in the peacefulness and appreciating the beauty of the place.

Douglas looked across at Lise, smiled broadly and nodded. He thought that there were times when it is not necessary to comment. They both realised that this special place had only become accessible because they had ventured off the well-trodden path.

Back in the office, Douglas and Lise sat down, a little dishevelled but with contented looks on their faces.

"Would you like to have a peek at what that meeting COULD be like if people were prepared to step off the path?" Lise asked Douglas.

Douglas was in no doubt. "Definitely," he said, beginning to feel that now they were getting somewhere. Lise fiddled with her mini computer and a scene appeared on the screen.

Everyone at the meeting sat enthralled as Ellie outlined her cost-cutting scheme and her ideas on increasing sales. The cost-cutting centred on new ways of purchasing, and on sales around new methods of targeting. Most people in the meeting were amazed that Ellie had come up with these ideas, as she had only worked at *Guardian Angel* for six months, and had had very little other work experience since leaving university.

"What fabulous ideas!" Mike exclaimed when Ellie had finished. "I suggest you present this to Jane as soon as possible." Jane Williamson, manager of the new Executive Business team, an operational team whose responsibility it was to generate new business, was Ellie's boss. Everyone nodded in agreement. A couple of people even tapped the table to emphasise their approval.

"I think we should implement the sales ideas as soon as we can," Ann suggested.

"It'll keep us ahead of our target for the quarter. We're already 6% up and this should give us another boost." Ann's comments also brought forth murmurs of approval from the others around the table.

"Douglas will be delighted to hear about these new ideas, and as keen as we are to see them implemented," said Bill, before moving on to the next item of business.

Lise switched off the scene and turned to Douglas. "Better than before?"

"Wow, much better. I can't believe it. What a difference! Everyone seemed focused on supporting each other, and really keen to take the new ideas forward. Is this possible in reality, Lise, or was that pure fantasy?" Douglas looked apprehensive. He didn't think of himself as a cynic, but he did have a healthy scepticism.

"What do you think?" Lise threw the issue back into his court.

"It's obviously what I want, I'm just not sure if it's possible," he responded.

"Most people didn't believe air travel would ever be possible, yet we now take it for granted. As before, it depends on how much you want it to happen."

"Oh I do, I definitely do," Douglas replied immediately. And he meant it.

"Lunch?" Lise suggested.

Chapter Eight

More to Things Than Meets the Eye

"Man is made by his belief, as he believes, so he is"
Bhagavad Gita (500BC)

OVER A LUNCH OF SANDWICHES AND SALAD, WITH FRUIT juice followed by decaffeinated coffee (Bett had placed the order with the local deli – she was always careful to ensure that Douglas ate healthily whenever he had a 'working' lunch), Douglas reviewed what had transpired so far. He was keen to take stock and see where this investigation was leading them. He had found the first phase fascinating, if a little revealing of his own part in holding the company back. Now he wanted to probe a little deeper, to discover and understand why he and his colleagues often got stuck in their conditioning and why they found it difficult to see a way out.

Lise agreed to spend the first part of the afternoon developing his understanding of this issue.

"Do you know what mechanical blindness is?" Lise launched into the next session.

"I'm not sure," said Douglas, who'd been taken a little by surprise at the abrupt reconvening of proceedings.

"You know what cataracts are?" asked Lise.

"Yes. They often affect the eyes of older people," replied Douglas.

"People can also be born with cataracts. This is sometimes referred to as mechanical blindness."

"Right," said Douglas, who was, as he had often been before, a little bemused by Lise's use of an apparently obscure starting point for their work together.

"Before doctors understood this, people afflicted with cataracts remained blind throughout their lives."

"Hmmm, sad," commented Douglas softly.

"So how do you think those first patients reacted when they had their cataracts removed and the bandages taken off?" Lise asked.

"They must have been ecstatic to be able to finally see the things that, no doubt, people had described to them previously. To at last see colours and shapes would be absolutely brilliant."

"What if I told you that they begged the doctors to make them blind again?"

"I would say that was incredible. Why on earth would someone want to be blind?" Douglas's puzzlement was obvious.

"Because all they could see was a swirling mass of colour. They were confronted with a cacophony of colour without any shape or form. They found it terrifying."

"How could that be?" Douglas replied. "Surely they were able to see what everyone else could see, what we can see now?"

"But they had no reference points to make any meaning out of what they saw," Lise explained. "They hadn't been taught to know what to see."

"So all they saw was the colours which made up the objects. Is that what you're saying?" asked Douglas.

"Yes, that's right," Lise continued. "You remember how parents introduce their children to new objects, by pointing to them and repeating their names – like pointing to a cow and saying 'cow'? The child then repeats the word and makes the link between the shape and the word. This goes on from a very early age as we introduce our young to the world they live in."

Although Douglas had been married for 21 years, he and Pat had no children. Just as well, he had often thought, as he was so committed to his work at *Guardian Angel*. But he could, of course, recall many times when he'd witnessed the scene Lise described, as he was uncle to various nieces and nephews and had also watched his friends' children grow up.

"The same process of making meaning out of what is happening around us also takes place as we grow up. We learn to make meaning out of everything that is happening out there. This is our process of social conditioning." Lise was in full flow once again.

"Can you be more specific?" Douglas asked Lise.

"Take another everyday example. Say you're driving on the motorway and you see a lane closure ahead with the inevitable contraflow. You've slowed down and you're sitting in the long queue of traffic waiting to get through. As you're sitting there you see the 'bad boys and girls' speeding past in the empty lane, hoping that they will be able to squeeze in further up. What do you make of that?" Lise quizzed Douglas.

"What do I make of that?" Douglas repeated the question as a prelude to demonstrating exactly what he made of it. "Anything from 'arrogant fools' to 'self-ish and childish behaviour'," he said, fuming at the very thought.

"And what do you say to yourself in such circumstances?"

"Like I said, 'arrogant s***'. There's no way I let them in if they try it on me." Douglas's skin colour had now changed to a light crimson.

"And how do you feel?"

"Bloody angry, that's how I feel," he went on.

"And what do you do?" Lise continued to probe Douglas.

"I make sure I drive as close to the car in front to make sure they can't sneak in front of me."

Lise was interested in his use of language, especially his use of 'sneak' to describe the other driver's movements. "What if that person you're trying to stop getting in front of you is a doctor on-call trying to get to a patient who is seriously ill, or someone trying to reach a hospital to visit a dying relative?"

"That would be different. In that case I'd let them in." Douglas relaxed a little. "But they're not, are they?" Douglas said, his belligerent attitude re-emerging.

"How do you know they're not?" Lise asked Douglas, with that little smile on her lips and a twinkle in her eyes.

"I suppose I don't really know," he admitted, grudgingly.

"So you make it up. Is that what you're saying?" Lise sounded a little bit like a prosecuting counsel. Must ease off a bit or I'll antagonise him, she thought.

"I suppose I do in a way," conceded Douglas. "But doesn't everyone?"

"Probably a lot of people do. But I wouldn't say

everyone does. I'm trying to show you that what happens in the world only means something to us when we confer meaning on it by what we pay attention to. Our feelings are the result of how we process information through our unconscious filters, how we self-dialogue it and create internal images. Our feelings are our emotional responses, which, in turn, cause our reactions. All this takes only a fraction of a second while remaining unconscious. Do you follow me?" Lise asked, taking a deep breath.

"So, you are saying that I could feel differently about these drivers if I became more conscious of my internal processes, and changed my interpretation of the situation? What are these unconscious filters you mentioned?" asked Douglas.

"Well, the answer to your first question is, yes. We can change the meaning of what's happening in our outside world, and our filters are where real change can be initiated. By sticking with the ones we have, we continuously head off on that 'well-trodden path' we've already walked on."

"Tell me more about my filters." Douglas leaned forward, fascinated to hear more.

"Anything we can experience through our senses – the things we see, hear, touch, smell and taste will be channelled through our filters as we make meaning of them. Through our early life-conditioning we learn what to see, hear, touch, smell and taste from parents, teachers and peers. We also learn how to behave in certain circumstances. I always wonder at the aggressive behaviour, which parents sometimes display when their children are in the car with them. A great lesson for their children, don't you think?"

"Yes, it does seem a bit counter-productive to me," Douglas responded, although he didn't want to be too judgmental of parents, having no children of his own.

"It also happens in organisations where young managers learn their management behaviour from their seniors. Many trainee managers simply copy that very same behaviour, once they themselves become managers, despite having been critical of it before. More of that later though. The main filters to our reality are our values, beliefs, rules, our developing ego and past experience – the latter extending from pre-birth to the present time." Lise went to the flip chart and wrote down the filters:

VALUES
BELIEFS
RULES
EGO
PAST EXPERIENCE

"You used the term 'filters to our reality'," said Douglas, interrupting Lise. "What do you mean by that?"

"What we make of our circumstances becomes our reality. In other words, what we pay attention to is what we ultimately experience, and the sum of these experiences becomes our reality. What we pay attention to will be determined by our current filters. We constantly filter out potential data that doesn't fit with our 'map of the world'."

"'Map of the world'? What in heaven's name is that?" Douglas's scepticism was showing itself.

Lise ignored the urge to comment on Douglas's use of 'heaven' in relation to his question. "Our map is our internal representation of what is happening in the outside world. You see, most people believe they live in the outside world when, in fact, we live in our own internal world of representation. You remember how we agreed you could change your representation of what the drivers were doing on the motorway?"

Douglas nodded.

"In effect, you have changed your map of the world for that particular situation. And as a result you would no doubt feel differently about it and act differently."

"Like waving him in front of me?"

"Yes, indeed," Lise continued. "And how would you feel then?"

"I'd probably feel pretty good about myself. Yes, I probably would."

"So in that particular situation you've created a win-win outcome and avoided raising your blood pressure by 'throwing away' your energy on a complete stranger."

"I'd never thought about it like that before," said Douglas, thoughtfully.

"Before we look at the filters in a bit more detail, let's look at something closer to home – in the business world." Lise thought it best to keep emphasising the relevance of their work to business.

"What does 'recession' mean to you, Douglas? What do you see when people suggest that the economy is going into recession?"

"I see falling sales, tighter margins, a smaller workforce, lower costs, tough times and worn-out managers, mainly."

"And what do you say to yourself about it?"

"That we'll need to draw back, work harder, spend less, cut training, reduce recruitment – the usual things, really."

"How come some businesses have managed to

grow during recessions? I exclude, by the way, accountants and lawyers from this category," said Lise, smiling. Her last comment was a little tongue-in-cheek, as she knew Douglas had an accountancy background.

"Luck, I suppose," replied Douglas. "Can't think how they could have done it any other way."

"What if recession meant something else to you other than what you've just told me?"

"Like what?"

"Like a signal to get better, think sharper, change strategy, outperform competitors, work more closely as a team, things like that."

"Why would recession mean that? We all know what recession means, don't we?"

"Ah!" Lise felt she was getting to the point. "So who says recession has to mean any specific thing to anyone? Those companies who grow in recession obviously see these market conditions as an opportunity, especially when almost everyone else is battening down the hatches for the storm ahead. They then have the opportunity to stand out from the competition. Perhaps recessions are excuses to ease off and perform below our potential?"

Douglas wasn't totally convinced of this, although he was interested in how *Guardian Angel* managers could change their thinking so as to benefit from a recession. Nice thought, he mused, without being convinced it could be turned into reality.

Chapter Nine

Filters

*"The events of childhood do not pass but repeat them-
selves like seasons of the year."*

Eleanor Far Jeon

DOUGLAS WAS KEEN TO HEAR MORE ABOUT FILTERS.
They seemed in some way to hold the key to his
understanding the change process. Reflecting on the
beginning of his 'journey', as Lise had called it,
Douglas once again began to wonder why he had
never quite managed to get the company to perform
as well as he knew it could.

"I'm still confused as to why we can't get the company to work as successfully as I think it should,"
said Douglas, shaking his head. "For some time now
we have publicly recognised that our people are our
greatest asset. We have even included this in our
Company Values Statement."

"And do you, as a company, act out these values?"
Lise asked.

"What do you mean, 'act out'?"

"Are the decisions you make within the business,
including strategic decisions, made with reference to
these values?"

"A difficult one to answer," responded Douglas. "Generally speaking, our main concerns are related to market place conditions, our profitability and our value as a business."

"All key elements of taking the business forward, without a doubt. And do you also review the implications for your people? The training and development required, the current skills and knowledge levels, the effect on motivation, team spirit and stress levels, for example?"

"We usually leave that to the managers concerned." Douglas was feeling challenged and he could feel himself becoming defensive.

"Strange also that businesses should refer to people as 'assets', as if they were commodities like buildings, equity and so on," commented Lise.

Douglas shook his head and sighed, a sigh, which symbolised his frustration with what he viewed as semantics. What difference does this really make?

"A huge difference."

Douglas looked up, realising again that Lise had read his thoughts.

"Language is the biggest determinant of our reality," Lise continued. "The way we language our world creates our personal reality."

Douglas cringed at her use of 'language' as a verb, hardly noticing the irony of his reaction.

"By referring to people as assets, as with commodities, you have to perceive them as assets and ultimately treat them as such. It's similar to calling your people 'human resources', where people become a resource."

"So what do we call them?" Douglas asked.

"Why not just 'people', or perhaps 'team members', or 'colleagues', something which refers to them as human beings rather than 'human doings'?"

"'Human doings'?" Douglas laughed.

"Yes, 'human doings'. Managers are mostly concerned with what people do, not who they are," explained Lise.

Douglas wasn't completely sold on these ideas, but at least he was prepared not to dismiss them out of hand. He realised that they had only scratched the surface, and he was still keen to dig deeper and seek further insights. He turned to look out of the window.

"Enjoying yourself?" asked Lise, interrupting Douglas's contemplation. She had been watching him for a couple of minutes. "You look deep in thought."

"Sorry, just reviewing where I was to date and considering the possibilities for further insights."

"Good," Lise said. "Because this next part could be a little dry. But I'll do my best to spice it up for you."

Douglas knew she would.

"We'll deal separately with each of the individual filters I've mentioned. The bad – or good – news, depending on how you perceive things, is that there are many more unconscious filters working through us than we have time to deal with right now. What I've done is isolate key filters, to provide you with both a basic understanding of how filters work in general, and with some more specific knowledge of the impact these key filters have. Let's look at values first. Do you understand what these are?" Lise asked Douglas.

"Well, we spent plenty of time and money on getting our company values sorted out. They're the things we stand for, the basis of our personality, sort of."

"Excellent. Spot on, really. At the individual level they are the unconscious triggers for our personal motivation. For example, take life values. If health and fitness were an important value in someone's life, then they will have no problems in motivating themselves to eat healthily and exercise frequently. They'd just go and do it. For those people who keep wishing they could do something about their health and fitness and never really do, a good strategy would be to review their values and include this one in their set, or move it closer to the top of their list of values."

"Ah. So because I value work so highly in my life, I have no problem in getting in early and staying late. Is that correct?"

"Yes it is, although gaining a balance in life is also pretty important. Would you like to experiment with your work values?" Lise asked.

"Definitely," replied Douglas.

"This will give you more insight into your own change process. Got a pen and paper handy? Right, I'll ask you one question only and I'd like you to write down your response. Here goes. What's important to you about work?"

"What's important?" Douglas repeated.

"Yes, what's important to you about work? Take your time. Make a list of about eight or ten items, then we'll write them up on the flip chart."

Ten minutes later Douglas read out his list in no particular order, just as they had come to him, the way Lise had suggested.

His list included:

- teamwork
- achievement
- satisfaction
- financial success

- respect
- motivation
- responsibility
- choice
- variety
- people
- recognition

"Any idea what your number one work value would be?" asked Lise.

"I think it would be achievement," replied Douglas. "But how would I find out for certain?"

"That's a task for another day, a bit further down the line. But just suppose that financial success was your top value and teamwork your last one. Then suppose you were in a meeting with a colleague who also had these values but, on their list, their values' places were reversed, so that teamwork was top and financial success was last. Can you foresee any challenges in discussing new business strategies together?"

"We'd probably have a bit of a tussle. I'd be emphasising the need to ensure financial success, while my colleague would be more concerned about the effect on teamwork."

"You both ultimately want the same thing really, so you wouldn't be disagreeing on that. You would be having a conflict over values. When you understand this better you can reduce the level of destructive conflict that often takes place in management teams, and increase the focus on joint values and goals. So can you see the importance of our values as a filter?" Lise asked.

"Yes," Douglas replied. "When we are confronted with an issue we filter it through our values to place it, if you like, on our scale of importance, defining how much it means to us."

"Exactly!" Lise nodded her approval. "Can you see how this can also be related to the business?"

"Yes. If 'people' were truly within our values, our decisions would be made with reference to the impact on our people?"

"As well as other values, of course. The key is that everyone involved understands this, and the way their own values relate to company values."

Douglas could see the logic in this, although he recognised it could be a big challenge to get his team to that level of awareness.

"Have a look at this now." Lise flicked the switch and the mini computer screen lit up. "Here we have Tom about to attend a business social function where he doesn't know anyone else who will be attending. Tom is pretty nervous and worried that he may be left out on a limb with no one to speak with. Let's watch."

Tom enters the function room rather gingerly, keeping his head down and furtively seeking out faces he may recognise. He makes his way to the drinks table, keen to get something to hold on to. Taking a glass of white wine, he strolls as nonchalantly as possible across to the window and looks out.

"I'll put him out of his misery." Lise switched the film off.

"What do you think Tom believes about himself in relation to meeting strangers? That they will be keen to meet him, or that he's pretty uninteresting and no one will want to meet him?" Lise asked Douglas.

"The latter, most likely. Looks as if he has little confidence in himself in these situations," he replied.

"Now take a look at Tom in the same situation but where he believes that everyone in the room will want to meet him." Once again Lise switched on the film.

Tom strides into the room, head held high, smiling and making eye contact with numerous people as he heads for the drinks table. One or two people actually turn round to look, so strong is his presence in the room. Tom picks up his drink, makes eye contact with a couple of people close by and goes straight across to them, shakes hands and introduces himself. The response from the other two people is very positive – they look pleased that Tom had come to talk to them. Lise switched the film off again.

"Same situation, same function, same people, yet a very different outcome. So what happened to make it different?"

"Obviously his behaviour was different."

"Why was that – knowing what you know about him?" Lise asked.

"Tom probably perceived the situation differently because he was working through a different belief about himself and therefore perceived himself differently."

"Perfect! You're working well!" Lise exclaimed. "You can see then how we filter information through our 'beliefs', and how that ultimately changes the 'results' we get."

"Change the belief and change the result." Douglas could again see the logic, although it did seem a bit like common sense to him.

Lise had a mischievous grin on her face as she flicked the switch for the film to restart. It began with an ordinary street scene in which a young man and woman walked along the street towards the camera. The man was walking on the inside of the pavement, the woman on the outside. Lise switched the film off and turned to Douglas with a serious look on her face.

"What did you make of that?" she said.

"Only that the young man has not been taught that he should always walk on the outside of the pavement when walking with a woman. No manners, obviously." Douglas grinned at Lise because he knew that was what she had expected of him.

"Thanks," said Lise, acknowledging Douglas's response. "The man doesn't have the same set of 'rules' for that situation as you do. Correct?"

"Indeed."

"So you can see how when you filter that event through your 'rules' you get a different outcome?"

"The correct one, obviously!" Douglas replied, laughing.

"Beliefs and rules are closely related and, as with values, apply similarly to organisational filters and individual filters. A business which believes in itself and what it is doing will project confidence to the outside world. People will feel the business's energy and be attracted by it. As for rules, most people will have been told at some time in their work life that 'We don't do that round here', or that 'This is what happens in this department'. Do you see the connection?"

"I do see the connection, clearly, and I am beginning to see the significance of this in relation to the behaviour of the senior team."

"Excellent." Lise felt that they were really gaining momentum. "We'll deal with your ego filter later. I have a little surprise for you for this one."

At an earlier stage in their work together this may well have worried Douglas a bit. He now just felt excited anticipation.

"Have you ever heard a piece of music and said something like, 'I really like that', as you smiled to yourself?" Lise was moving on to complete the first stage of understanding filters.

"Often," said Douglas, nodding and grinning almost as if he was listening to such a piece at that very moment.

"And what makes you smile and enjoy music in this way? It may well be the intrinsic quality of the music. Could it also be something else?" Lise looked quizzically at Douglas.

"It could bring back memories of when I heard that particular music and remind me of my enjoyment at that time."

"Where are the memories brought back from?" Lise asked.

Douglas was getting used to what he would previously have thought peculiar questions, so he easily put aside any judgement and reviewed the query based on his expanding awareness.

"From my unconscious mind, I expect," offered Douglas, finally.

"You expect correctly! As you already know, our unconscious minds hold our memories and our 'software' upon which we draw. So when we hear a piece of music, our unconscious mind will hold the memory of the context in which we previously heard it, or heard it for the first time, and will access the emotional association which we have created and which we hold in relation to the music. So we get a good feeling every time we hear this music because of the strong association we have created over time."

"This can also work against us, when we hear something which has a negative association?" Douglas asked.

"Yes, indeed. And if you extrapolate this across our experience of life you will see why 'the past', as in our experiences – or more importantly, our interpretation of our experiences – impresses upon us in the present. And again, of course, why it is extremely challenging to break these associations and make 'real changes'. To change we have to find ways of letting go of the past associations which hold us back in life. The biggest problem for us is that over time these associations become part of us, and ultimately we believe they are us."

"It is quite common to hear people saying something like, 'I can't help it, it's just the way I am'. Is this what you're getting at?" Douglas asked, leaning forward, again demonstrating his ability to pick up and understand these new concepts quickly.

"Spot on!"

"Can you give an example?"

"Okay. Let's take public speaking. Many people fear the prospect of standing up and presenting in front of others. Yes?" Lise asked.

"I believe that's so," replied Douglas. Although he had grown pretty confident in such situations over time, he could still remember feeling afraid when he was younger.

"One reason – and there are many other possible reasons – can be that their fear is related to an incident experienced at an earlier time in their life, an experience which they have perceived as causing them to feel stupid, to be laughed at or ridiculed, etc when speaking in public. It could have been something which occurred with their friends as a youngster, for example. Once the association has been created it will become strengthened over time, until the individual believes that they are not the kind of person who can speak confidently in front of others."

"Unless they waken up," remarked Douglas, smiling.

"Yes, unless they waken up and are prepared to let go of this past association, which in turn has become part of their set of beliefs about their self."

"Even without your prompting," added Douglas, looking rather smug and pleased with himself, "I can also see how past associations affect current behaviours in organisations, and how these associations are passed on through the organisation. Like the belief, 'This is just how our industry works, it's always been like that, and always will'. And, unfortunately, to some extent that's the way I have thought over the years."

"Until now, of course."

"Absolutely!"

Douglas and Lise both sat back and enjoyed the moment.

"A good start!" Lise exclaimed. "We'll come back to this later. There's something interesting happening on the third floor in Marketing. Would you like to see?" Before allowing Douglas to reply, Lise continued, "I have a feeling there's also going to be something going on later on the fourth floor."

"Let's go," said Douglas, heading quickly out of his office suite towards the lift, which would take them swiftly and silently to the third floor. Douglas felt energised, although still somewhat bemused by some of the revelations he was experiencing. This is more fun than I've had in a long time, he thought.

"After this we can take a look at why most people stop having fun and begin taking themselves too seriously." Lise smiled again, her eyes dancing with delight at the thought. She certainly hadn't lost the knack of having fun, or really putting her positive energy into life's activities.

The lift opened on the third floor and Lise pointed

to a door halfway down the corridor on the left. It was the office of Mike Duncan, who had featured earlier in some of the film clips they had watched.

Chapter Ten

Pulling Rank

"The thrust of the warrior's way is to dethrone self importance."

Carlos Castenada

DOUGLAS AND LISE SLIPPED INTO MIKE'S OFFICE AND stood in the far corner where they could see everything that was going on. Douglas was getting used to being invisible, just like some of the characters he had loved reading about as a boy.

Mike had just come off the phone. He had been asking one of his assistant managers to come up and see him. They were actually on the same floor, but Mike always used this language when he wanted to see someone. He thought it set the scene, especially when we wanted something from them. A few moments later there was a knock on the door.

"Come in," Mike shouted from behind his desk.

"Hi." Mike's assistant greeted him as she came in.

"Alyson Green is responsible for the market research relating to new product development," Lise told Douglas. "Alyson's been with your company for four years. She's bright, but currently doing a job that doesn't challenge her any more. She needs and wants more responsibility, some more opportunities to apply her innovative mind to develop new products, and in the future, new marketing strategies."

Douglas nodded his approval. Alyson was just the kind of bright young manager he wanted in the company.

Alyson was just over five feet tall, with short black hair and dark brown eyes. She had an intensity and energy around her, which she transmitted to the people with whom she worked. Although small in stature, she portrayed the impression that she had something special to offer, and that she was a strong person who would not be easily put down.

"Alyson, I'm putting together some plans for our new with profits bonds and need your market research report urgently," said Mike.

"How urgent is urgently?" Alyson responded calmly.

"By close of play tomorrow." Mike was fond of using modern business jargon.

"That's impossible." Alyson sat up in her seat looking considerably taller than her five-feet-something. "I've already been asked to complete another key report for tomorrow, and I have to attend an important meeting tomorrow morning. It's just not feasible to make a decent job of another report as well. Remember we did agree at our last team development day that we would be able to say 'no' to you, when a demand was unreasonable."

Mike had been sitting back in his chair, hands clasped behind his head, staring past Alyson throughout her mini 'presentation'. He leaned forward when she had finished and removed his glasses. His cheeks were slightly flushed. "Look Alyson, I'm not asking you to do this report, I'm telling you. And if I have to pull rank to get it done then so be it," said Mike in a threatening tone. "I don't care what we agreed at our last meeting, I want this report and I want it by tomorrow evening."

Douglas's mouth dropped open again. What did he mean he didn't care what had been agreed? What was all this 'pulling rank' nonsense? Didn't he realise that he was talking to a valuable colleague of whom the company had high hopes? What way was this to treat any colleague, for that matter? How does all this fit in with our much-vaunted company values statement? And this was the person who had dismissed his presentation at the last conference. Douglas was becoming livid with anger when Lise slipped him a little piece of paper. Douglas took it from her, noticing as he did, that his hand was shaking with anger. There was a short note typewritten in the middle of the page:

"We do not see things as they are: we see them as we are."

Douglas took a deep breath and managed a little smile. He looked at Lise, nodded his approval and recalled the famous piece that his father would frequently quote from Robert Burns, the Scottish poet:

"O wad some pow'r the giftie gie us to see oursels
as ithers see us!
It wad frae monie a blunder free us, and foolish
notion."

Alyson's face, normally slightly tanned in colour, had gone white. She sat looking at Mike without saying a word for what seemed an immeasurable period of time. "And that's your last word?" she asked, finally.

"It is indeed!" Mike replied, leaning back in his chair and putting his hands behind his head again in what, Douglas thought, was a very self-satisfied pose.

Alyson rose slowly, nodded to Mike, turned and walked smartly out of his office.

I could wring his neck, Douglas thought. We could lose Alyson if we continue to treat her like that. Douglas had been meaning to talk to Mike about the level of staff turnover in his section, but hadn't quite got round to it. He made a mental note to do so within the next few days. Lise turned to Douglas and suggested they move on quickly to the fourth floor, where he might see something else which would interest him.

Interest me? A major understatement, Douglas thought. What more was there for him to see? What kind of company was this? Douglas and Lise quickly climbed the stairs to the fourth floor, turned right at the top and slipped into a room a few yards down the corridor. Just behind them came Jane Williamson, manager of the new Executive Business team. There were six people in the team, all middle managers apart from Jane, who was more senior and sat in on strategic project development at executive team level. They were reviewing new business performance to date, at the end of the third quarter.

"Great news," said Jane, opening the meeting on an upbeat note. "Overall, we're currently 23% ahead of target for the year. Effectively we have almost reached our annual target with just under three months to go. At least that's the good part of it. What worries me a bit is if we continue on this track until the end of the year we'll be almost 30% ahead of our budgeted income, and you know what that means."

"We certainly do," replied Richard Todd, a slightly greying, tired-looking manager. "We'll get stung on our targets for next year."

"What do you mean?" Bob Graham asked. Bob was new to the company. After completing his marketing degree he had worked in a direct marketing agency for three years before joining *Guardian Angel* as a junior Business Development manager. His enthusiasm and industry had been one of the main reasons the team had performed so well.

"Well, instead of congratulating us on our success, senior management will probably reckon they set our targets too low for this year and push them up much higher for next year," Richard explained. "They'll expect us to achieve them with very little increase in numbers."

"That's okay," Bob responded. "We're well able to increase our business if we continue as we've been doing. Sounds like an exciting prospect to me."

"Sounds depressing to me," chipped in Amanda Hall. "I'm going as hard as I can right now. I just don't fancy the prospect of facing much higher targets next year. I say we ease off for the last quarter so that we just top our target and no more. Give ourselves a bit of a break."

Douglas couldn't believe what he was hearing. Senior people in the company were suggesting that they ease off on new business. What the hell do they think they're doing?

"Remember, you're part of this scenario," Lise whispered. "Just the same as a football coach can't divorce himself from the actions of his team, neither can you divorce yourself from what your people do. We'll talk more in a few minutes when we leave."

Douglas would have much preferred to have materialised in front of them and told them exactly what he thought.

"I can see both sides of the equation," said Jane. "It

is great that we've done so well, but equally we have to be careful we don't shoot ourselves in the foot by going over the top. I would favour easing off over the next three months so that we finish the year around 5 – 10% ahead. It'll mean being not quite as aggressive as we've been in generating business so far this year."

Almost everyone nodded their approval, with the exception of Bob. He sat shaking his head.

"You're not happy with this?" Jane stated the obvious.

"I think it's crazy. You're suggesting that we actually limit our performance for the next three months. What kind of message will that convey to our customers, our competitors and the City – that we've reached our limit? Don't forget that once you start this kind of tactic, it can be difficult to reverse it. Before we know it we'll be working even harder just to stand still."

There were a lot of 'You'll learn' looks around the table. A few looked a little uncomfortable, and most were unmoved.

"That's all very well in theory, but we're operating in the real world," said Amanda, who had a 'We've seen all this before' look on her face. "What Jane suggests will keep everyone happy. Senior management will be pleased that we've over-achieved our targets, we'll get a good bonus, plus we won't have a huge hike in our targets for next year. And the outside world will see that the business has grown over the past twelve months."

"Hear, hear," Richard sang out, rather cynically.

"Time to go," Lise whispered to Douglas, who was once again doing his impersonation of a drowning fish.

Back in his office Douglas poured himself a glass

of water and tried yet again to calm down.

"Where do you want to start?" Lise asked him.

"At the moment I'm feeling stunned and angry at what I've just seen. I can't believe that people behave in this way. It is counter-productive in both cases. First we have a manager who 'pulls rank', forcing a colleague to produce a report she doesn't have time to complete. And then we have a team who agree to under-perform for three months. What's happening here? It's just as well we're the only ones who have been able to view these scenarios."

Lise flicked the switch on her film machine and the screen lit up. "Take a look at this," she said.

It was a film taken in Douglas's room. Douglas was sitting behind his desk, spectacles dangling from the end of his nose, pouring over a pile of papers on his desk. "Come in," he said, responding to the knock on the door. "Sit down, Mike." Douglas pointed to a chair on the other side of his desk.

Mike sat down.

"I've been reading through this draft," Douglas continued, without looking directly at Mike. "It'll need to be completely redone. It's too long, it's imprecise and it doesn't provide a summary of the key outcomes."

Mike sat silently and nodded in response whilst thinking that he had done the report in exactly as Douglas had requested. Being used to this sort of 'change of mind', he didn't even bother getting into a discussion about it. "When do you want it back?" Mike eventually asked.

"By 5pm tomorrow at the latest". Douglas was still looking through the papers.

Mike's heart sank. He'd already promised his wife that he would take her out for a meal that evening to celebrate her birthday. As he was involved in a major client presentation the next day, this development meant that he would have to stay on late this evening to re-work the report. There was no point in debating the issue with Douglas. He expects devotion to duty and would probably 'pull rank' if I did object, thought Mike. He nodded again. "That's fine," said Mike. "You'll have it on time."

"That's all," Douglas said, without looking up. Mike stood up and made his way out of the room.

Lise switched off the film. They both had been privy to Mike's inner thoughts as well as the external dialogue.

"I don't know what to say." Douglas looked sheepishly at Lise. "I was really under pressure that day and had masses of work to get through."

Lise looked at him sympathetically. She knew he would be suffering some pain at what he had seen. "Thinking back to that scenario you've just seen, why don't you jot down the things you could have done better? Is that okay?" Lise asked.

"Yes, sure. It will be useful – painful but useful." Douglas took out his pen and began to write.

After ten minutes he looked up. "I think I've got almost everything down, though it did take me some time to go over the scene in detail again."

"Will you share your thoughts with me?" Lise asked.

"Sure. I've made a little list. I'll just go through each point as they come. Here goes." Douglas took a deep breath, letting the air out of his lungs slowly.

"Fine." Lise smiled.

"When Mike came into the room I should have stood up, welcomed him, shook his hand perhaps and apologised that I had a little more to read before starting our discussion. I could also have either put my specs on properly or taken them off altogether. I looked rather pompous the way I had them.

When I shared the information about the report, I could have made proper eye contact with Mike. In fact, I should have come out from behind my desk and sat down beside him, and I should have asked him for his views on the report. Perhaps if I had done this he would have been willing to share his true feelings about it. I could certainly have asked him to decide when he would be able to re-hash it. Come to think of it, I did have some flexibility regarding its submission. I also see that I didn't really give him a clear impression of what I now expected from the report.

At the end of our meeting I could have got up, thanked him for coming to see me and for his continued contribution to the company and then seen him to the door."

As Lise began to speak, Douglas raised his hand. "You don't have to point out the connection between my own behaviour toward Mike and Mike's toward Alyson. I can see that clearly now." Douglas took a deep breath as if it had been the first breath since he'd started his monologue.

"Whew," signed Lise. "Be careful not to beat yourself up over this, Douglas."

She hadn't used his name for some time and Douglas found it made quite an impact.

"Otherwise you will simply repeat the patterns you have followed unconsciously for years," continued Lise. "You should congratulate yourself on having noticed how you can now do things differently, and that by doing things differently you will begin to create a better culture around you. There is no guarantee that other people will immediately change their approach when you change yours. Over a period of time, though, others will find it almost impossible not to change their approach, provided that you are consistent and persistent in changing yours. Can you see that?"

"I can see how I'm likely to get very frustrated if I change and others don't follow immediately. I suspect I will have to be patient, otherwise I could easily drift back to the 'well-trodden path'." Douglas smiled as Lise showed her delight that he was beginning to integrate all he'd learned.

"Great!" Lise exclaimed. "Now you're moving. And you're right. Once people see that your approach has changed, and that it's permanent, they'll also start moving. Some people will move faster than others and there will be some in need of a bit of a gentle push."

Douglas experienced a real feeling of liberation, as if he had truly let something of himself go. He felt exhilarated until the memory of the middle management team meeting came rushing back. "I recognise my influence in the incident between Mike and Alyson, but I am still puzzled about the other scenario. How on earth could I have had an effect on that?"

Lise flicked the switch and the screen once again came back to life. This time the setting was the boardroom. Douglas was sitting at the top of the table, his executive team down each side.

"Next item on the agenda is the new business results for the first six months," Douglas announced. Once again his spectacles were balanced on the end of his nose, and he wasn't making any significant eye contact with anyone in the team. Douglas cringed as he watched himself.

"Good news," Jane began, "we are 19.3% up against our annual target for the year to date, with prospects looking good for this trend to continue throughout year."

"Hmmm," Douglas mumbled.

"Just how realistic do you think your targets were?" asked Jeremy Dunn, the Finance Director.

"What do you mean?" Jane asked.

"Well, it looks like we've set your targets too low if you can beat them so easily, don't you think?"

"I suppose that's one way of looking at it," responded Jane, looking and feeling rather deflated. "But I reckon the biggest part of it is down to the hard work, creativity and commitment of our team."

"Hmmm," Douglas repeated. "Perhaps we should keep a close eye on this and reassess our targets for next year in light of these results. On to the next item…"

Jane sat back in her seat looking a little dazed and confused, wondering what they had to do to get some recognition for their efforts.

"Enough!" Douglas exclaimed, looking even more depressed than before. "I can't believe what that looks like, Lise. I just can't believe how unconscious we can be of ourselves and the impact and influence we have on others. It's no wonder Jane adopted the approach she did at that first meeting we saw. During that session my first reaction was to reprimand her and insist she listened to Bob's opinion on the matter. I didn't realise the part I had played in influencing her point of view."

Douglas was slowly becoming aware of how unconscious we are of our own actions and their effect on others. Although he was still sceptical, Douglas was moving in the right direction and beginning to wonder how he could get others to start to wake up.

"I would urge you to stick with changing your own approach for now. It's too easy to try and project your own understanding of consciousness onto others instead of concentrating on it for yourself," explained Lise. "It would be helpful to remember that what we see outside of ourselves that we don't like is a projection of what's inside ourselves that we don't like. Once you learn to stay with it yourself the rest will follow. Then you can start to plan an awakening for your colleagues throughout the company."

"So how do I become more conscious? Is there a technique to make this possible?" Douglas was on a roll.

"Do you notice how quickly we can race back into unconsciousness?" asked Lise.

"Now you're losing me," responded Douglas, looked mildly annoyed.

"Well, we have become conditioned to expect an instant solution to any challenges we are faced with. The pill that cures a headache or the diet that miraculously makes you slim, and so on. There are certain activities that you can introduce to your life on a regular basis in order to effect change, and this is only part of the story. Becoming more conscious is a moment by moment challenge. We must observe ourselves in action and begin the process of 'not doing'. This is the challenge for all of us, and one which is well worth the effort. Shall we continue with this tomorrow?"

Douglas had been lost for the last few minutes, deep in thought. What Lise had revealed to him had certainly opened his eyes, making him aware of the need for him to change. Douglas's feelings ranged from elation at these awakenings, to depression at the thought of what else he would discover. He decided elation was the more productive emotion to stay with. He smiled to himself as he realised he was indeed becoming more conscious of his own possibilities. Douglas looked up to say goodbye to Lise only to find that she had already gone.

How do I learn 'not doing'? Douglas pondered.

Chapter Eleven

'Not Doing'

" 'Not doing' involves being fully alert all the time whilst observing one's emotional responses carefully."
Theun Mares

"GOOD MORNING!" ONCE AGAIN, LISE WAS IN Douglas's office before he even realised it. "How are you today?"

"Ah, not too bad," replied Douglas.

"As good as that?" Lise joked.

"Well, 'not too bad' is okay for me." Douglas was getting a bit ratty. Lise noticed this and decided to leave this issue for another time.

"Remind me to do some more work on language with you, Douglas," Lise responded.

"Haven't we got other things to look at first? Like 'not doing'?"

"Yes." Lise wondered if a good starting point would be to use the language issue as an example. But looking at Douglas's face, she decided against it. "Let's take 'not doing' as a starting point for today. Remember we looked at the scenario of the lane closure on the motorway?"

"Yes, I do. You pointed out how I could change the

meaning of the person trying to squeeze in front of me having driven up the outside lane almost to the contraflow."

"That's the one. Do you remember how you feel on these occasions?" Lise asked.

"Bloody angry, as I've already told you," replied Douglas.

"Do you think that your reaction is a direct result of these emotions?"

"What do you mean?"

"Well, do you usually act angrily when you feel angry?"

"Well, of course. How else would you expect me to act?"

"Can you see now what I mean by 'not doing'?" Lise continued.

"I'm not sure. Do you mean that when I feel angry, I don't have to act angrily?"

"Yes, that's more or less what I mean."

"It's a pretty difficult task to stop yourself."

Douglas considered this for a moment, then had a thought. "I can relate that to situations where I'm aware that what I'm about to say to my wife will make her angry, yet I carry on and say it regardless."

"And we think we're free!" Lise laughed. "Isn't it funny how we get ourselves caught in our own prisons? 'Not doing' is a challenge for all of us and it's not possible unless we become more conscious."

"Again that sounds much easier than the reality. What does 'becoming more conscious' really mean?"

"Noticing yourself more is a start." Lise realised that this was a crucial stage in Douglas's process of transformation. She knew that his logical-rational mind would require an in-depth rational explanation – a tall order for something that really has to be experienced to be understood.

The great eastern philosophers and Zen Masters refused to be drawn into any requirement to articulate their knowledge. Knowing that to do so is illusory, as real knowledge is experienced within rather than from some outside source.

Zen Masters were often asked difficult and convoluted questions by their disciples. For example a monk asked Chao Chou (one of the greatest Chinese Zen masters who lived until he was 120) "The myriad things return to one. Where does the one return to?" Chao Chou replied "When I was in Ch'ing Chou I made a cloth shirt. It weighed seven pounds." In other words he was providing an answer in the form of a puzzle or koan (as they are known) in order to challenge the questioner to find the answer for themselves.

"Noticing and paying attention to your physiology – your body, your feelings and your emotions – allows you to begin to make choices, and thereby increase your personal power," Lise continued. "Notice also your self-dialogue. I can't emphasise enough the level of impact that your self-dialogue has on your current experience of reality. When we begin to notice this, it again will bring us to the point of choice – knowing that we can change our self-dialogue and become aware of what is productive for us and what is not."

"Can you give me an example of this?" Douglas asked.

"I will in a moment," replied Lise.

"There is one final element of 'not doing' which tends to oversee all the others – learning to live in the present moment, the 'here and now'. This allows us to notice whether our emotions are authentic for the current circumstances, or if they are products of our past, but which we carry with us in the present. Also, by being in the moment, we put ourselves, our soul energy, into whatever it is we are doing."

Hmmm, thought Douglas, this is getting rather 'New Age' for me. Douglas carried on with his thoughts, before once again realising that Lise would know exactly what he was thinking. So he did what he was beginning to realise would help his people to live more effectively: he articulated these thoughts and feelings to Lise.

Lise, knowing what was going on, looked both sympathetic and proud that Douglas was opening up in this way. "Isn't it funny how we like to label things?" she said. "And often we make them the same as something, thereby filtering out any new meaning and leaving us with what we already have. By labelling this 'New Age', as you put it, you can then avoid noticing what could be in it for you."

"I'm beginning to see that, and I'm beginning to realise why we have never really embraced real change at *Guardian Angel*."

"Let's look, then, at the antithesis of living in the present, at some of the everyday things which people say and which distract them from really enjoying the moment. Have you ever heard – or maybe even said – something like, 'I'll be glad when I get this over with'?"

"Heard if often, and yes, probably said something similar many times."

"It is endemic in our culture, so much so we even have a restaurant chain called TGI Friday – Thank God it's Friday. And we hear people say at the end of the week, 'Thank God, that's another week over with.' I wonder if they'll want all those weeks back when they're lying on their death bed," Lise said, grinning at Douglas.

"Yes, I can admit to language like that occasionally. I can also remember how my mother always wanted to get a meal 'over with' and tidied up rather than enjoy the meal itself. Maybe we should start a restaurant called TGI Mondays to start to change things."

"Why not?" Lise responded. "It would maybe wake us up a little as to how we currently live. Isn't it strange how we attach meaning to words? For example, we invent the concept of a week, give each day a name, and then get happy or depressed depending on what day is coming up. Maybe we should change the names, or call every day by the same name. So how will this concept help us in the workplace?"

Douglas's mind returned quickly to the task at hand.

"Have you ever walked into a hotel or restaurant and just felt you knew it was going to be good?" Lise asked.

"Yes, although less often than I would have liked," replied Douglas.

"And you've indicated that at other times you get the opposite feeling?"

"I also get the 'neutral' feeling. What I mean by that is that they provide an acceptable level of product and service, without really hitting the mark."

"Do you notice the difference in energy that you experience in these contrasting places?"

"Yes I do actually, although I've never thought of it like that before."

"It's as if, in the 'good place', people want to be there – if you like, be 'present'. Whereas in the 'less good' establishments they're just doing the job to get finished."

"Just going through the motions," Douglas added.

"Yes, exactly. In the first instance their energy is going into the moment. They are putting their heart and soul, as we say, into their work, and bingo! The result is a superb experience for everyone. Unfortunately at present there seems to be vicious cycle of non-care in our culture, including in our organisations. Non-care, that is, about the real outcomes which affect us all: about people's lives, how they live them and how we create productive, living communities. Many organisations have other priorities – they care about profit, shareholders, share prices, about stoking and stroking egos, whilst expecting their workforce to care about these things and about their customers. We see the results of lack of care in many areas of our lives – train crashes, gas explosions, child abuse, and many others. Safety mechanisms in trains were not introduced in the UK in the late-eighties because the ratio of deaths to potential costs was too high. In other words, not enough people had died to make it cost-effective to introduce a life-saving mechanism. Jobs have become a means to an end instead of being fulfilling in their own right." Lise took a deep breath and noticed that Douglas was in a very thoughtful mood. "Gosh, I was getting a bit carried away there."

"Wow," Douglas said at last. "And we're part of it, aren't we?"

"Yes and no." Lise was being careful not to paint a totally bleak picture. "Having worked here for two years, although I've seen a lot of this non-care in action, there is also a good deal of caring behaviour going on. I believe that, ultimately, given the opportunity and 'permission', all people will put their heart and soul into what they're doing. The crucial thing

I've noticed is that when we are in the present moment we can discover energy in whatever activity in which we are involved. When we operate in this way, tasks are completed more smoothly and effectively, with plenty of energy left over to deal with the real challenges when they occur, as they will. But that's another story."

"What was the bit about our emotions being authentic, then?" Douglas's logical mind wanted to make sure he didn't miss out on the explanation of something he had made a mental note of.

"Do you ever still 'go in a huff'?" Lise asked.

"Hmmm. Yes, I suppose I would have to own up to having feelings of petulance. Strange creatures that we are." Douglas smiled.

"So when did you learn to do this?"

"When I was a child, of course. Don't all children go in a huff to get what they want?"

"I can't confirm whether all children do it. But I can confirm that it is used as a tactic to get what we want. These are child-like feelings and behaviours to which we have become so attached that, despite being adults, we still act in a child-like fashion. So, what I'm saying is that, as an adult, when we stay present, we can note that this emotion is not authentic for us right now and we can choose to act differently. That way we can be more productive, for others and ourselves. Do you want to see a quick example of this here at *Guardian Angel*?"

"Yes, please." Douglas enjoyed seeing the 'theory' in action. Lise flicked the switch of her mini computer and a picture appeared once again on the screen.

It showed a meeting of sales managers who were gathered to develop some creative ideas for their direct sales force. David Fleck, the senior manager in charge of Direct Sales, was chairing the meeting. Keith Harris, the newest Sales manager, who had been recruited recently from a close competitor, was speaking.

"I believe that what our consultants need is more autonomy – a real feeling of running their own business. We could invite entrepreneurs in to give them guidance and build new business skills. What do you think?" Keith asked.

"We've just about had this empowerment stuff up to here," responded David, lifting his right hand just above his silver rimmed half moon glasses to indicate that he was 'going under'. "What I think we need is some good old fashioned management. Sit on them hard, keep them on their toes and make them realise that if they don't meet their targets their jobs will be under threat."

"Hear, hear!" A couple of other managers chorused in agreement. Keith was tight-lipped as he looked down at his papers. Well, if that's what I get for coming up with new ideas, I may as well shut up, he thought.

"Any further business?" David's voice faded out as Lise turned the film off.

"That looked like the first stage," said Douglas. "He acted out on his old emotion, he went in a huff. Yes?"

"Yes, he did. He chose not to challenge David's view and began to retreat into a non-contributing mode. Now, he could come out of that state in time, yet in his eyes he has been discounted by his manager."

"I wonder how many times over the years I've done that to someone?" Douglas asked himself. "I certainly hated these types of, what do you call them, discount, when I was younger."

"David was acting out on his past emotion. Let's take a look at what happens when he operates in the 'here and now'."

Douglas and Lise watched the second film, which picked up the same incident just after David Fleck's response.

"Before we move on, David, I'd like to make two points. Firstly, I would appreciate it if my ideas were given more careful consideration and some debate before being discarded. Secondly, with reference to your own view, do you have any up-to-date evidence to support your opinion on how our sales consultants should be encouraged to achieve results? Because there is growing evidence of the success of the strategy which I have just presented."

David was slightly taken aback and responded a little defensively. "I'm sorry if I offended you, Keith. That's just my style – brash and aggressive."

"Thank you for your consideration, David. I don't feel offended. I just want to make sure my views can be heard in these forums and given a reasonable airing, so that I can make a contribution to the future success of the team. I don't expect all my views or ideas to be taken on board, only listened to."

Lise flicked off the switch again and turned to Douglas who was sitting with a broad grin on his face.

"Well done, Keith," said Douglas. "I can see the complete difference in the responses. I could also see the change in David. He had to take notice of Keith because he sensed, as I did, that Keith would stick calmly to his point even if he did go into aggressive overdrive. And you could see the change in mood of the others in the team. It was as though they thought,

'Wow, someone has challenged David at last', although one or two had the 'Who does he think he is?' look on their faces."

"An excellent example of 'not doing'. Keith felt the old emotion and then chose to act out differently and got a different response from David and the team. One of the awarenesses to develop here is our role as an 'observer' of ourselves. Rather that being 'driven' by our senses and emotions, we can make a more conscious choice of how we can act out. It's a bit like waking up and finding that we can slow down and change direction if we want. Have you heard how eastern philosophers described this process?"

Douglas shook his head. "But I'm sure you're going to tell me," he said, laughing.

"Showing you will be more effective, I think." Lise stood up and walked towards the door. "This way," she said, signalling to Douglas.

"Hold on! What the hell's happening here?" Douglas shouted.

He couldn't believe it. One minute he was in his office, the next he was inside a carriage being pulled along at breakneck speed by six thoroughbred horses: three brown, two white and one black.

"This carriage is out of control. Tell the driver to slow down," Douglas pleaded with Lise.

"This is *your* life," replied Lise, smiling at the ambiguous use of this phrase. "You tell him."

"Excuse me," Douglas shouted to the driver, who was urging the horses on to even greater speeds. "Can you slow down a bit? This carriage is almost out of control."

"Who the hell do think you are?" replied the driver. "I've been running your life for forty-six years without a word from you. What's the big deal now?"

Douglas sat back down looking white and just a bit frightened, his normal composure lost.

"What are we doing in this contraption with that madman driving the horses? Who the hell does he think HE is?" Douglas was shaking.

"He is your ego," replied Lise.

"So who am I then?" Douglas was both angry and confused.

"You represent your true self. Some call it your higher self. When the true self awakens, it can, as the ancient philosophers said, take over the reins. Until then, the ego will drive you on to where it wants to go. Ever heard people boast about how 'driven' they are?"

"Yes, indeed." Douglas certainly recognised this sentiment. He had often used it about himself and had bemoaned the fact that not enough of his team were like- minded. "But right now I'd feel safer if these horses were under my control, either directly or indirectly."

"All in good time," replied Lise. She put her hand on his arm to help calm him down. "You have to make the decision for yourself. Do you want to remain driven or do you want to be the driver?"

"Well, of course I want to be the driver. What do I do to get him under control?"

"Firstly, be firm and assertive with him to get the horses under control. Then you can begin to make the decisions about speed and direction yourself. At times you may still choose to move swiftly but, in future, this will be under your control."

Douglas cleared his throat, took a deep breath and knocked loudly on the roof of the carriage. Putting his head out of the window, he caught his breath once again with the speed they were travelling.

"What do you want now?" Douglas's ego demanded.

"I want you to rein in the horses immediately, slow them down gradually and pull up at the side of the track." Douglas spoke clearly and authoritatively.

"Okay," said his driver, reluctantly. "But I hope you know what you're doing. Without me, you'll be lost."

"I'll take that chance for now." Douglas felt a real sense of self as he spoke, realising that they were slowing to a canter, a trot and then finally coming to a halt. He became aware of his heart beating loudly in his chest and his breathing, which was deeper and more even than normal.

"What now?" Douglas asked Lise.

"Your shout," she replied, laughing at her choice of phrase. It was slang, but entirely suited to the moment. "Just give your driver some initial indication of how you want your relationship to be in the immediate future and you can then take it from there."

"What now?" shouted Douglas's driver.

Douglas and Lise both laughed on hearing this.

"What's all the laughing about? I've a job to do here," said the driver.

Douglas leaned out of the window, relieved that he could now speak without shouting. "I'd like you to park here for a while until I decide where I want to go next." Douglas again sounded very assertive.

"You're making a big mistake," responded his ego. "You're going to have to give up a lot if you don't take me along with you. You probably don't realise how much you've depended on me over the years, more so since you've progressed in business. The titles, cars, parking spaces, name plates and much,

much more. All down to me, you know."

"As I said before, I'll take that chance for now. And we can come to some longer- term agreement on our relationship later." Douglas felt completely in control now.

"Please yourself. But remember, I'll always be here to fall back on if you need me," Douglas's driver muttered with a wry grin.

"Let's go!" Lise opened the door and stepped out of the carriage.

"Speak to you later," Douglas shouted to the driver, as he too stepped out of the carriage and straight back into his office.

"So what's more fun – 'being driven', or getting into the 'driving seat' and being in control?" Lise asked Douglas as they sat down.

Douglas was still re-orientating himself. He would need some time to take in the full significance of the experience. Was that really how it had been? Had his ego really taken over his life to such an extent? In future he would have to be more vigilant to make sure he knew who was driving whom.

"Being in the 'driving seat', obviously," replied Douglas to Lise's question. "And I was totally unaware of my ego being as dominant as it appeared today in that frightening experience. I already noticed, early in our discussions, how challenging it would be to give up my parking space, and I noticed in the films how pompous I can look and sound. So I suppose I can see it as a pretty dominant force within me." Douglas had always felt he was in charge, so it was a considerable jolt to find out and to accept that he may not always have been.

"What now?" Douglas asked, breaking spontaneously into laughter.

"Oh, nothing much. Just a few little things like giving up your parking space, your job title and your need to chair meetings, for starters. Then we can look at your share options, bonuses and other minor factors." Lise was also laughing heartily, knowing at the same time that Douglas had 'moved' as a result of this experience. "Time, I think, to look at how to get some fun back into the workplace."

Chapter Twelve

What's Happening?

"It is the capacity to accept pain, to persist in spite of results, not because of them, that is necessary in order to achieve anything permanent."

Rudi

"WHAT'S UP WITH 'DEADLY DOUG', THEN?" MIKE Duncan asked, leaning across the table in mock-theatrical style. He was sitting in the company restaurant having lunch with Bill Dow, Jane Williamson and Keith Harris.

"What do you mean, what's up with him?" Jane asked as she nibbled on her mixed salad, in another attempt to lose the extra pounds she had put on during her last holiday.

"Well, he's spent the last two days holed up with some good-looking female, doing goodness knows what. Do you think he's having a mid-life crisis? Someone even saw him laughing yesterday. They caught a glimpse of him from their window."

"Find that one a bit hard to take," said Bill, laughing, which was a surprise in itself to some of his colleagues sitting at a table nearby. *Guardian Angel* was normally a reserved kind of a place. People weren't especially unhappy, but there was never much real verve or energy about the place. Apart, that is, from a few individuals, mostly newer members of the company.

"Who is she anyway?" Jane inquired, looking around at her three male colleagues, whom she noted all looked rather worn-out and tired.

"Not sure," Mike said. "Bett Smith, his PA, said she was from our department. At least that's what Douglas had told her. Lise, I think Bett called her."

"Haven't come across anyone of that name. Must be one of the newcomers." Bill stopped quite abruptly. Leaning forward with a slightly bemused look on his face, as if he had just been give an impossibly challenging MENSA puzzle to work out, he asked, almost in a whisper, "What in heaven's name would Douglas be spending three days with a new member of the Marketing department for?"

"Why don't you ask heaven?" Keith responded cheekily. Keith is one of the new, more energised members of the team.

"Thanks," Bill responded sarcastically.

"Maybe she has dropped in from heaven to enlighten our esteemed boss and give him some insights from the other side," continued Keith, ignoring his colleagues' lack of appreciation for his humour.

"Thanks again," Bill said, looking a bit fed up with Keith. "Apparently he has cancelled his appointments for three days, including some pretty important strategy meetings. Can't fathom it myself."

"Maybe she's some high level consultant that Doug has engaged. You know how he likes to spend large sums on the big names. Could be one of those American management gurus," suggested Mike.

"Or he could be in therapy. He could do with it!" Ann Edwards had joined the group and added a cutting edge to the discussion.

"More likely an expert in mergers and acquisitions. You know these rumours of our impending take-over have been re-emerging. Maybe they're planning our defence, or our terms for a take-over," suggested Jane, looking worried.

"Not in the immediate future," Mike stated authoritatively. "Don't think the market's right for it. I'm sure we're making up stories. There will be a simple, straightforward explanation, I'm sure. Doug's not daft you know. Didn't get where he is without being a shrewd operator."

"Wish I had his salary," Ann said, sipping her coffee and looking as if she would benefit from some therapy herself.

"You could if you really wanted it," Keith suggested enthusiastically. His comment met with silence and an acid stare. He could feel the skin on his face prickle.

"I'm sure there will be a fairly simple explanation for it all." Jane broke the tension with an unconvincing suggestion, "Wouldn't it be fun to be a fly on the wall when he's with her? A real eye-opener, I'm sure. Maybe that's it. She's a TV producer come to discuss doing a fly-on-the-wall programme at *Guardian Angel*."

Everyone round the table sat up and looked at Jane in amazement.

"That would be a real bundle of laughs for the viewers," said Keith, bursting into spontaneous laughter at what he thought was a fabulously witty comment. No one else seemed to find anything he said even remotely amusing.

"There's no way I would be involved in something like that," said Ann, adamantly.

Now there's a surprise, thought Keith. I'm sure the viewers would also be relieved to know that. But this time he kept his thoughts to himself, realising the unenthusiastic response his humour was receiving.

"I don't know," Mike commented. "It could give us some low-cost exposure, as long as we were all on our best behaviour, and as long as they were restricted from meetings and other situations which might supply our competitors with key information."

"I don't think they let you do that. I think you have to give them a pretty free hand once you let them in. Otherwise it wouldn't really be a fly-on-the-wall experience." Bill seemed to know what he was talking about. At least he always sounded like he did, Keith thought.

"I've often thought it would be fun and interesting to be able to sit in on other people's meetings. Imagine the insights it would give you," said Jane, looking more animated that usual.

"Just as well it can't happen," said Ann. "Some of our meetings are pretty uninspiring. A waste of time, most of them."

"Why is that?" Keith inquired.

"Never get anything done. Some days its meetings, meetings, meetings. Same old stuff again and again without any real outcomes. I'd ban meetings if I were in charge," Ann replied.

"Why don't we make the meetings more effective then?" Keith probed again.

"We've all been on courses at some time or other to run meetings better, but nothing ever happens. You go back into meetings and the people are just the same. Whoever shouts the loudest is the one who is heard. And if you do come up with a good idea, it is either not listened to or you're told to shut up and keep your crazy ideas to yourself." Ann was on a roll.

"It's not as bad as that." Keith was staying with it. "Surely if we were all determined to get better at meetings, they would improve. After all, it's the people who make meetings. Meetings don't exist without us."

"You've obviously been on some course recently. You'll learn." Ann signalled that she'd had enough of this line of argument and looked across to Bill for support. Bill just shrugged his shoulders and took another sip of his coffee.

"Why doesn't a volunteer agree to go up and ask to see Doug today?" Jane asked, changing the subject. Her idea was greeted by silence, broken eventually when Mike responded.

"Great idea. Off you go then!" he said.

They all laughed briefly, afraid to draw too much attention to themselves.

Jane stood up at that point to head back to her office.

"Maybe he's writing a book?" Jane suggested as her parting shot, before turning on her heels and walking off.

Chapter Thirteen

Get Serious

"The problem is that as people hide behind their masks, they become defined by them and are unable to tell the difference between what is natural and what is not. Sometimes they become so profoundly disconnected from the true self they think their mask is their true nature."

Malidoma Patrice Some

"WHAT'S THIS ALL ABOUT?" DOUGLAS HAD AGAIN been whisked away from his office and was now sitting in a plane with Lise beside him. Lise had insisted he take the window seat.

"Just sit back and enjoy yourself," she ordered. "When was the last time you looked out the window of a plane?"

"Can't remember. I usually take the aisle seat; it gets me out of the plane faster. What would I want to look out a window for? I know what I'll see. I've seen it many times before." Douglas was resisting Lise's attempts at making this a fun experience. He travelled regularly by plane, with an average of one return journey per week, so he was used to the routine.

Outside the plane it was a dull, wet and misty day. Douglas would have described it using a good old Scots word – dreich. The plane had taxied out to the runway while they were talking. Although used to flying, Douglas was not used to walking out of his office and straight into a plane. This whole experience with Lise was quite astonishing, he thought.

At the end of the runway, the engines revved up before the pilot headed for take off. As the nose of the plane lifted and headed upwards, turbulence caused by the heavy low cloud started. The plane bucked and swayed its way skywards.

"Keep watching!" Lise said, digging her elbow into Douglas's ribs as he had begun to look around the plane in an absent-minded way. He was pleased that on this journey he didn't have the usual pile of reports and papers to wade through on the way to his next meeting.

"What?" Douglas asked, smarting slightly from Lise's good-natured blow.

"Just keep looking out the window. Look, you can see the cloud is lightening a bit, can't you?"

Not an earth-shattering observation, Douglas thought. He wondered what the big surprise would be.

"Sure can," Douglas replied quite sarcastically to Lise's question.

Just at that moment the plane cleared the heavy grey cloud and soared upwards beyond the cloud base.

"Wow!" Lise was excited. She was craning over Douglas to see the cloud formation. "Look at the blueness of the sky and the brightness of the sun – it's almost blinding. Take a look below. Isn't that cloud just like newly fallen snow?"

"So what am I supposed to see now?" Douglas had fallen back into his slightly pompous state. I've seen this all before. What's new?

"Don't you think it's amazing that in only a few moments we moved through all that grey heavy stuff into bright sunlight? Isn't it amazing to think the sun shines every day? Only some days the cloud covers it up, and then we use this as an excuse to moan. Just as well, I suppose. If we didn't have the weather to moan about, what would people talk about?"

Douglas noticed an almost child-like excitement in Lise's voice, something he could only faintly remember himself. He was always too busy getting things done to get excited about simple experiences like this one.

"You've never seen what's out there before, Douglas," Lise continued.

"How do you come to that conclusion?" Douglas responded.

"Each day is different. Each cloud formation is unique. The colour of the sky is unique to the moment. The colours reflected by the sun are a 'one off'. Look and you'll see the differences. Each time of day is different in terms of light and colour. Each time of year is different. Each moment there will be something changing. After all, we are travelling at more than 400 miles per hour. This is why, when we say we've seen it all before, we close ourselves off from the infinite possibilities available to us. And the fun!" Lise sparkled with life.

Douglas had started looking, and he turned to Lise with an almost excited smile on his face. "It's amazing. Just for about ten seconds there I could see the shadow of our plane on the clouds below, as if it was escorting us through the skies. And what was even more amazing was there was a beam of sunlight following the shadow across the clouds like a spotlight." Douglas was becoming more interested in the idea of taking at least a few moments to appreciate the possibilities around him.

"Most people are too busy being who they think they are to observe what's really happening around them," said Lise. "This is another simple example. Like your sitting position, this is an opportunity to become more conscious in everyday life." Changing tack, Lise asked Douglas, "During which period of your life do you reckon you learned the most, at the fastest pace?"

"What do you mean exactly?" Douglas replied.

"Well, if you take your life in five-year blocks, say 0-5, 6-10, 11-15 and so on, which of these periods was the most significant for your learning?"

"Probably 0-5, when I learned to walk, talk, read, write, draw, ride a bike and many other things. Is that what you mean?"

"Yes, 0-5 years is a most prolific learning period in our lives. Psychologists call the period between 0 and 7 years the imprinting period when much of our personality and perceptions are established. We could look into this in more detail another time. I'm more interested in other matters at the moment." Lise changed tack again. "Was learning fun for you in those early years, if you can remember? I mean, can you remember having fun while you played and learned?"

"Definitely. Before going to school, that is. I remember feeling great excitement the first time I was able to read a full page of a book completely by myself. And I was ecstatic when I realised I was riding along on my two-wheeler bike on my own for the first time. That's not to say that I haven't had exciting moments in my life beyond that stage; it just seems that they have become few and far between."

Douglas turned and looked out the window again, smiling. His face lit up when he smiled spontaneously, Lise noticed. His eyes became alive, his uneven teeth showed and the skin on his face seemed to 'waken up'. His colour changed from a sort of dull bluish-grey – he had heavy beard growth – to a lighter pink translucent colour. Lise thought it was a pity he couldn't see himself at that moment. Of course she also knew that she could make that possible for him.

The plane was coming into land. Douglas was relieved. He'd had a vision of himself and Lise parachuting down as another means of gaining more insight.

"Another time maybe?" Lise smiled.

Douglas's mouth broke into a wide grin once again. He'd forgotten she could read his thoughts.

Must really remember to watch what I'm thinking, he thought.

"A good lesson for us all," said Lise, continuing to evaluate Douglas's thoughts. "Paying more attention to what we are thinking and beginning to choose what we want to think would be of great benefit to everyone. Despite the fact we all have an infinite capacity to think, most people have mostly the same thoughts every day of their lives. That's why they keep attracting the same things into their lives and complain that they don't have enough." Lise was getting carried away – veering off on another track. Better keep focused on following through with what we started on the plane, she thought.

"Oops!" Lise said, putting her hand over her

mouth. "I'm heading off at a tangent, again."

"I get the point, though," said Douglas. "I'd like to pursue this further if we can, maybe tomorrow, or at a later date?"

"Yes, we will," confirmed Lise.

The plane had now stopped and they got up to disembark. As they reached the start of the walkway, which stretched, from the plane to the main airport concourse, Lise signalled that they were turning left rather than following the signs to 'Arrivals'. She opened the door that lay ahead and walked back into Douglas's office.

They'll never believe this, Douglas thought. He was beginning to feel adventurous again, and excited about what was coming next. He seemed to have stopped fearing what he might find out and had started looking forward to it.

"Have a look at this." Lise flicked the switch on her mini computer and the film screen came alive with pictures of a very young baby in a pram. Two adults were leaning over the baby, making the usual weird baby noises that adults produce: lots of 'coochie-coos' and those interesting sounds that are made by running your fingers up and down over your lips.

"Ever done that?" Lise asked Douglas.

"What? Lie in a pram and watch adults make fools of themselves?" Douglas burst into spontaneous laughter. He was getting the hang of this, he thought.

"Touché!" Lise laughed. She was delighted to see how engaged Douglas was in this process.

"Yes, I have also done the adult bit," Douglas said.

They turned back to the film, which Lise had paused while they were talking.

"Look, he's laughing!" one of the adults said.

"Are you sure? Maybe he's got a touch of wind," the other suggested.

"No, he's definitely laughing." Both adults, who looked as if they could be the child's grandparents, were absolutely delighted at this momentous occurrence.

"Isn't it great how people, no matter how serious they've become themselves, are always enthused about getting a child to laugh?" Lise turned to Douglas as she made her observation, having once again paused the film.

"Yes, I've done it often," replied Douglas. "It kind of shows that the baby is alive and connected to us. And, of course, enjoying its life."

Lise flicked the switch on again.

"Same child a few years on. He's about five in this clip," said Lise, introducing the next film.

The boy was standing with his head slightly lowered as he listened to a lecture from an elder. As the adult turned slightly you could see that it was the man who had previously been making the child laugh. Standing slightly off to one side was another youngster, a girl of a similar age to the boy, possibly a little older. As the adult continued in ultra-serious mode, the little boy couldn't resist a look at his friend. His shoulders started to quiver as he worked hard to keep his face straight and serious. But it was to no avail; his smile eventually broke through.

"Take that stupid grin off your face, boy," the adult growled, "and get serious. You won't go far if you don't stop giggling and learn to take things more seriously. Life isn't just a big joke, you know."

"Pretty confusing, don't you think?" Lise asked Douglas. "One minute everyone wants the boy to laugh and enjoy life, the next he's told to get serious and take the smile off his face."

"Yes, I can remember that well." Douglas smiled. "So often as a child I was told not to be cheeky, not to laugh when adults were talking, and to sit quietly and behave myself."

"There's obviously a need for a child to know when it's inappropriate to laugh and giggle, but they must also learn to take advantage of the many opportunities to let go and have a laugh. You've already agreed that you learned faster when you were young and having fun than at any other time in your life. Agreed?" Lise looked at Douglas for confirmation.

"Yes, definitely," replied Douglas.

"People always learn faster when they're truly engaged in an activity and are having fun, fun being used here in the broadest sense of the word. It doesn't necessarily mean falling about with laughter. You can have fun successfully chairing a vibrant meeting during which new and interesting strategies emerge. Take a look at the next clip."

Lise started the film rolling again. The scene this time was a boardroom, which Douglas recognised immediately as his own boardroom at *Guardian Angel*. He himself was sitting at the head of the table chairing a meeting. He remembered the meeting well: it was a 'look back – look forward' meeting which aimed to assess the strategies of the previous year and look ahead to uncover new opportunities for the future. It had been a particularly turgid meeting. No one seemed motivated to bring forward new ideas; there were no sparks.

Douglas and Lise watched the film for a few minutes. Lise had asked Douglas to observe the behaviour of the people around the table: their physiology – body language and facial expressions – and their language, as well as the content of their discussion.

She switched the film off again.

"Not much fun to be seen there." Douglas thought he would make the point before being asked.

"Looks as if they're all suffering from 'terminal professionalism'," suggested Lise.

"Terminal what?" Douglas enquired.

"A condition brought on by people who believe the more important they become, the more serious they have to be," Lise explained, smiling.

"Lots of glasses half-way down noses," laughed Douglas, knowing that he was one of the guilty ones. He also noticed that the way for him to find a release from the condition was to laugh at himself. He wondered whether this could be his 'true self' re-emerging to take over from his 'ego' – the 'great one' who always looked serious and sounded profound, and who always had to have strategic-sounding answers to the questions he was asked. Lise noticed that Douglas actually looked much younger during this moment than he had done in the film they'd just seen.

"We all looked so wooden in the meeting, Douglas complained. "How can we make the change?" Asking the question, Douglas realised that he was discovering the 'how' himself. He was experiencing – or re-experiencing – a 'new me' through this work.

"I've just realised," he said, "that what I've been looking for for so long were solutions in the form of processes, procedures, strategies and the like – tangible measurable elements, just as they teach you at the top business schools. I've been looking for the answers out there when they were with me all the time. The problem I will have is in convincing my colleagues that what I'm experiencing is real change. The kind of change that will, when embraced by us as a company, change our culture significantly and open up our people's true potential."

Lise wondered if Douglas's choice to use the word 'people' instead of 'staff' had been a conscious one.

"Yes, 'people' not 'staff'," Douglas continued. "It sounds much more human, I think."

Lise was taken aback for a moment. Was Douglas reading her thoughts now? Better watch, just in case.

"'Staff' is an army term," said Lise, agreeing with Douglas's sentiment. "Comes from the stick or staff officers carry under their arm."

"Where is this taking us?" Douglas asked.

"Where would you like it to take us?" Lise replied, and they both laughed again as Douglas realised how easy it was for him to slip back into his 'normal' mode.

"We started out in the plane to show that when we stay open – child-like, even – we get the opportunity to experience awakenings. "

"Like when the plane breaks through the heavy grey cloud and into the open sky?" Douglas asked.

"Yes. We have that 'Aah!' moment when we realise, for example, that the sun does shine 365 days a year."

"I just had a similar 'Aah!' moment, or awakening, when I realised that our solutions lie inside rather than outside. I've heard the words before and we've discussed it before, but I hadn't really experienced it until that moment. I can understand why the Zen masters believe that these experiences can't really be verbalised. We have to experience them. In some ways it's like learning to ride a bike."

"Yes, it's the 'Aah!' moments that will bring your meetings to life and bring people's lives to life as they look out through new eyes at the infinite possibilities open to them. Having fun?" Lise asked Douglas.

"Definitely!" Douglas confirmed, looking out the window at the sky and smiling broadly. "Have we got time for more today?" Douglas asked Lise. But as he turned to face her, Douglas found Lise had already gone. He was relieved to see the door through which she had left was slightly ajar; it confirmed that Lise did indeed exist. He sometimes had to pinch himself to prove that he was experiencing all of this.

"Do you need anything before I go?" Bett was standing at his office door, her arms folded across her chest.

"No, I'm fine thanks, Bett," replied Douglas, smiling.

"I'm not sure anyone else is smiling around here," Bett said. By now Douglas was no longer surprised by this observation. "I've got a pile of messages from your senior colleagues wanting answers to their questions. Do you want to call off your third day with this girl and deal with the work waiting for you?" Bett asked, emphasising 'girl' in a pejorative tone.

"Definitely not." Douglas was adamant. Maybe they'll start working out their own answers, he thought, knowing that he had been partly responsible for their dependence on him.

"I've had a real fun day today," Douglas said, smiling again at Bett.

"Okay," she replied. "I'll leave you to it." Bett turned and walked out the room, shaking her head in disbelief at what she had just heard. The Chief Executive had had a 'real fun day'. She couldn't believe her ears.

Douglas tidied his desk and prepared to leave, and decided that he would take a stroll before driving home.

The *Guardian Angel* head office was situated in a developing business park with some open spaces and walkways. Douglas occasionally – generally after a hard day – would take a stroll for five minutes so as to freshen himself up before driving home. It sometimes helped him to release any stress that had built up over the day.

Today was different though. Douglas felt quite exhilarated, yet he was mystified. He was not sure whether he could really believe what was happening to him, but his eyes had certainly been opened, most importantly to himself. His developing realisation that real change lay within himself rather than with others was the biggest awakening. Douglas had, of course, heard this suggestion before and, to an extent, understood it. What he realised now was the difference between understanding something at an intellectual level and really knowing it – really feeling it inside. He noticed how, in the past, change had always been something for others to get involved in, sometimes after attending a seminar by Tom Peters or some other business guru.

No point in going through this awakening without doing something differently, Douglas thought. He had already observed that he was sitting differently more often and that he was now a calmer driver. But because he wasn't following his normal work routine, he hadn't had any real opportunities to do things differently at work. Or was that just another excuse? Douglas smiled to himself as he arrived at his car.

Chapter Fourteen

A Road Less Travelled

"Sell your cleverness, and buy bewilderment."

Rumi

DOUGLAS PARKED HIS CAR IN HIS USUAL PLACE, RIGHT beside the executive lift and stairs to the seventh floor, and headed for the lift. About to press the lift button he stopped himself. There was no one around so he turned and walked back to the car, got back inside and sat down.

What had just occurred to Douglas was how unconscious he had been since driving into the car park. He had worked to stay conscious during his drive in, and he had noticed how this had heightened his anticipation of the day ahead. After that he had become unconscious and had gone into automatic pilot as he drove to his space, parked his seven-series BMW, took his case from the back seat and walked to the lift.

Two thoughts popped into Douglas's mind as he reviewed his actions. What if he drove his car into the general, first-come first-served car park instead? And what if, instead of taking the lift, he walked up the stairs and through each floor on the way up? Douglas knew he would get a space in the other car park because of his habitually early arrival at work, and decided he would do this another day. He experienced a faint feeling of opting-out about this decision, but he felt he would focus on his second thought today. He was committed to change and would continually challenge his consciousness – in a supportive way – on a daily basis.

The *Guardian Angel* head office had two sets of stairs, one set at each end of the building. A large brick and glass construction built in the mid-80s, the office had been built to accommodate around 2000 people but now housed in the region of 2500, so space was a bit tight in places. Douglas's plan was to walk up to each floor, walk through the open plan offices and up the stairs at the other end.

In his five years as Chief Executive, Douglas had never done anything like this before. He was feeling nervous and could feel his stomach tightening a little as he headed up the stairs. Good exercise as well, Douglas thought, and he wondered what would lie in front of him and whether there would be many people around at this time.

Arriving at his office, Douglas sat down to reflect on his new experience. He had been a great supporter of one of management's buzz phrases, Management By Wandering About (MBWA) for a number of years, and he had encouraged his own senior colleagues to use it as a management technique. The realisation that this was the first time he had actually done it himself was not lost on Douglas. He also realised that most of the management education in which he had been involved was very technical. And rather than seeing it as a real opportunity to truly meet some of their colleagues, many managers just used it to create the illusion that they were doing something productive. Management education was often seen as an activity to be done, something to be ticked off on the daily or weekly list. Douglas could see that much of this 'stuff' often missed the mark whilst creating the illusion of change.

So how had his 'journey' been? Douglas looked out the window as he reflected on how it had gone.

"You're on the ball early this morning." Lise had slipped in to Douglas's office once again and was sitting on the seat beside his desk. "Tell me what your walk through the offices was like."

"The biggest challenge was to walk through as myself, you know, rather than as Chief Executive – to let people see a bit of me rather than just my ego. It's not easy, it's uncomfortable for both parties – uncomfortable for me as I had to remove some of my armour – that felt very exposing; uncomfortable for my colleagues as they have never really met me in any circumstance, let alone in this unexpected context. Come to think of it, I've only just been reacquainted with myself."

"What was the response like?" Lise asked.

"Well, I looked in on Mike Duncan. He was on his own at the time and he looked extremely surprised to see me, as if he had just seen a ghost. I explained that I had been engaged in important development work that would pay dividends for the company in the long-term. I told him I would brief people on the outcomes as soon as possible. I also said that I appreciated his own and his colleagues' patience over the past two days if they had been attempting to contact me."

"And what did he say?"

"Nothing to start with: he just did an impersonation of a fish. But eventually he said it was no problem and thanked me for looking in."

"Who else did you see?"

"I stopped off and said hello to whoever was in the office at the time. I had to introduce myself to one or two people who didn't know me, as they had only started with us a couple of weeks ago. I've always prided myself in having met all 'new starts' within their first week, so I was surprised and disappointed that I hadn't had the opportunity to meet up. They also looked surprised when they saw me – as if what I was doing was a major event!"

"How many times have you done this?"

"This was the first time."

"It's not really surprising that they were taken aback then."

"It made me realise how detached I am from the 'action' in the business. One person asked me if it was true that we were about to be taken over by another major financial services company."

"And?"

"Of course I said it wasn't true. Although I didn't say that we've had some preliminary discussions with another company."

"So how do you think you were received? What do you think people are saying about your little journey through the office?"

"Probably not a lot. Maybe they thought the lift had broken." Douglas laughed, again realising with pleasure that he was laughing at himself.

"Let's take a look." Lise stepped out the office, with Douglas close on her heels. By this time he realised that when she left, he followed. They went into the lift again and down to the staff restaurant. Douglas was also used to the idea of his being invisible in these circumstances. That was one reason why he had felt a little uncomfortable earlier.

"Over here," directed Lise, moving quickly to an empty table beside a small group of people who were deep in animated conversation. The topic? Douglas's morning adventure. A simple human act, but one which, to judge by the buzz of conversation, seemed to have taken on earth-shattering significance.

More than one group appeared to be in deep discussion, and Lise had chosen the one that seemed to include more junior people.

"I did!" exclaimed a fresh-faced young man called David Allan. "I spent five minutes talking to *the* boss this morning. I had come in early to finish off some urgent work and there he was in front of me, large as life, with his hand outstretched, saying 'Good morning' and introducing himself."

"Did you recognise him?" asked June Hegley, David's colleague.

"I wasn't sure at first, then I realised who I was talking to."

"What did he say? What was he doing there?" A chorus of questions arose from the assembled throng.

"Give me a chance." David was enjoying being in the limelight and was milking it as best he could.

"What do you think, so far?" Lise asked Douglas.

"I didn't realise it would cause quite so much interest," he replied.

Back at the table, David continued, "He asked me what I did, how long I had been with the company, if I enjoyed my job, things like that. Ah, and he asked me if I thought *Guardian Angel* was a good company to work for."

"What did you say to that?" David's colleagues asked.

"I told him that it was the first company I'd

worked for full time, so I had nothing to compare it with. I said it was an good place to work, as far as I could tell."

"And then what?"

"He quizzed me a bit further on my job, then moved on."

"So what was he doing?" June asked.

"I don't know, maybe he just fancied talking to the future Chief Exec!" This comment, predictably, was met with resounding laughter.

At least I've got them laughing, Douglas thought.

"I guess he just fancies walking through the office and meeting some people," David continued.

"Must be more to it than that," chipped in Stuart Adams, a slightly older member of the group.

"Over here." Lise pulled gently on Douglas's arm and took him to a table where Mike Duncan and some other managers were sitting. By this time the whole restaurant was buzzing. Everyone seemed to want to find out the significance of Douglas's morning walk.

"First time I've ever seen him do something like that," Mike was telling the group.

"I thought it was great," butted in Keith Harris from Sales. "I really enjoyed my couple of minutes chat."

Mike ignored Keith's comment. "Well, he told me he'd been engaged in some serious company development work over the past two days and that he'd tell us the outcome when he's finished. I think it's the take-over talks. We're definitely going to be taken over. He was just preparing the ground so that it doesn't come as too much of a shock. A cute move, I'd say."

"Maybe he just wanted to meet people and say

hello," Keith continued, undeterred by his previous rebuff. The assembled group just looked at him in silence with pained expressions on their faces and shook their heads in disbelief.

"Let's go back now. I've seen and heard enough," said Douglas, looking a little pained himself as he turned and walked away.

Back in the office, Douglas reflected on what he had just seen and heard. "It's probably much as I would have expected," he said to Lise.

"As I said earlier, you can't expect people to change their thinking as soon as you do something different. When they realise that this is not a 'one off' but part of what you do, they will begin to act differently. Even though there was the expected scepticism and some cynicism about your actions, there were some people out there who really appreciated seeing you. Focus on that, rather than those looking for the hidden agendas."

"Hidden agendas are so much a part of everyday organisational life, it seems an almost impossible task to remove them."

"Maybe they don't need to be removed, just changed," Lise said, smiling.

"How changed? What do you mean by that?" Douglas looked a little weary.

"I agree that hidden agendas are part of organisational life, and that the task of removing them seems almost impossible. And I wonder if the immediate task is to convert the current hidden agendas into more productive agendas, thus erasing the need for them to be hidden at all," replied Lise, using what she thought was a rather nice 'pacing' statement. This was something she hoped to introduce Douglas to if she had time.

"You've lost me now," said Douglas, looking weary.

"Look at Keith – his view of what you were up to was very productive. So, in other circumstances, when the Keiths of this world begin to predominate, they will start to change the overall thinking within the company. People will look for productive reasons for things happening rather than the more negative hidden agendas."

"You're being a bit idealistic, don't you think?" Douglas responded. Lise could see that he had slipped a little in his thinking.

"So, are you saying you're happy to continue with your current culture and continue to under-perform?" Lise challenged Douglas.

"Of course I don't want the business to under-perform. What a crazy question! I just think that what you're suggesting doesn't seem possible in the real world."

"So whose world is the real world? I used to lie awake at night worrying what the real world was going to be like, since the one I was living in seemed pretty challenging as it was. Remember our discussion on maps?" Lise asked.

Douglas nodded.

"Our map is our world, our real world. If you and, most probably your colleagues as well, cannot begin to create something new in your maps, in your world, then nothing will change for you in the outside world. The real challenge of change is overcoming our conditioning, and allowing ourselves to step from the known into the unknown. Most of the courses you have attended, books you have read, etc. have given you *information* about new possibilities. You will only experience change, as you already know, by stepping into the unknown. Like this morning's experience. And when we take action like this, it will invariably be met with cynicism and scepticism. As we've already discussed, this will eventually dissipate when people realise the change is permanent."

Chapter Fifteen

Bringing the Right into the Left

"The world shall perish not for lack of wonders, but from lack of wonder."

JBS Haldane

"SO HOW CAN WE STIMULATE REAL CHANGE IN *GUARDIAN Angel* and make it stick?" Douglas asked, still unsure how to make things happen in the company.

"Take a look at this." Lise switched on the film again. "This is a change programme which is running for some of your middle managers right now."

The scene was one with which Douglas was very familiar. The tables in the room were set out in a 'U' shape. Each delegate had a glass neatly placed on a white paper mat with a bottle of mineral water beside it. Bowls of mints were laid out at regular intervals, and delegates' names were written on little cards that sat in front of them. Up at the front were a flip chart, an overhead projector and a PowerPoint projector. Everyone, including the presenter, was dressed in a business suit.

"Notice anything familiar?" Lise quizzed Douglas.

"Looks pretty much like any other training pro- gramme I've attended. Nothing of any significance as

123

far as I am concerned. The presenter looks confident and is presenting in a well-ordered manner. The delegates look quite focused and intent."

"So, nothing out of the ordinary then?"

"No, looks like a well-run professional course to me."

"Can you see the irony in that?" Lise was smiling.

"In what?" Douglas appeared to be getting frustrated again with her line of questioning.

"That this is a change programme, yet nothing is really different," replied Lise.

"But they're exploring new concepts, aren't they?"

"And how would exploring the concept of riding a bike or playing a musical instrument or skiing help you to actually do these things?"

"That's different though, they are all physical or action-based. Our managers are learning about the management of change so they can implement change within their respective teams."

"I appreciate that your managers are learning to implement change for their teams. But I thought that what they would have to do as a result of their learning would be action-based, isn't that the case?"

"Yes, I can see what you're getting at, particularly with my recent experience of Managing By Wandering About (MWBA). Doing it was much more challenging than simply agreeing with the concept – and it made much more of an impact."

"So why are your programmes structured to resemble the status quo?"

"I'm not sure, but I am sure that you are about to tell me!" Douglas sat back and smiled for the first time during this discussion. He noticed that he had fallen quite quickly back into defensive mode again, but again he was here to learn, not defend his current reality.

"You probably know about the work of the brain researcher Roger Sperry, who won the Nobel Prize for his work on the varied functions of the upper right and left hemispheres of the brain?" Lise asked.

"I know a little, but please refresh my memory," replied Douglas.

"Sperry's research indicated that the right and left hemispheres have distinct functions. The left is our logical / rational side and the right the creative / imaginative. Let me expand on that a little." Lise stood up and walked over to the flip chart. She wrote 'LEFT' on the left side of the chart and 'RIGHT' on the other side.

She continued writing, ending with this list:

LEFT	RIGHT
RATIONAL	CREATIVE
LOGICAL	IMAGINATIVE
KNOWN	MYSTERY
PAST	MAGIC
EVALUATION	UNKNOWN
SAME	DIFFERENT
CONSCIOUS	FUTURE
	UNCONSCIOUS

When she finished, Lise turned to Douglas and asked, "So where is real change located?"

"On the right side."

"Where do you think most people in the workshop we've just seen are?"

"On the left side."

"And your left brain is constantly evaluating anything that is presented in order to remain on the left side. When do you reckon you spent most of your time on the mystery / magic side?"

"Same as you asked me about learning, during my first five years. I can still remember having this little friend who no one else could see. We used to play together for hours and, to this day, I could swear that there actually was someone there. Of course my parents and other adults just laughed. My father took me aside when I was about four and told me I had to stop playing these foolish games," said Douglas.

"How did you feel?" Lise asked.

"I was devastated. For a while I played secretly with him and then I had to give him up altogether. I also remember making clouds when I was young. I used to love lying on the grass in our garden and make beautiful clouds. I seemed to be able to make the clouds exactly the way I wanted them."

"And what happened to this great skill?"

"Went the same way as my friend. My father told me that I was too old to be doing childish things like making clouds."

"What age were you then?"

"Between four and five, probably nearer five. It was the summer before starting school and he said it was time I started growing up."

"What do you think about that now?"

"Looking at it now, cloud-making seemed a pretty momentous thing to do – 'cool', as my young niece would say. From the point of view of right / left brain, I can see how I was being pushed from the right to the left."

"Rightly so in some ways. Sorry about the pun, completely unintentional, honestly. We all need to be able to operate in the logical-rational world, so staying on the right side would always have its challenges. Can you imagine taking your invisible little friend into board meeting?" Lise asked.

"Might make them a good deal more interesting," replied Douglas. They both laughed heartily.

"What happens, as we've seen before, is that we are driven further and further into the logical-rational world and away from the magical and mysterious aspect of our existence; until our whole world has to be controlled, measured, justified and accounted for; until there is no room left for anything else, including real change, including mystery. I'm referring to the 'mystery of life', the mysteries that we normally miss, or rationalise in our left-sided consciousness. Take coincidences, for example. Ever experienced one?"

"Often, especially in situations where I've been about to phone someone. The phone rings and I find that the person I was about to ring has phoned me. Or sometimes, someone I haven't seen for some time comes into my mind and then shortly afterwards I bump into them."

"So, ordinarily, most people put that down to coincidence, which works pretty well in the left-brained logical-rational world."

"What else could it be?" Douglas asked.

"What if it wasn't a coincidence?"

"What do you mean?" Douglas quizzed.

"What if other unseen forces were at work? And," Lise continued before Douglas could answer, "these forces contrived to produce the outcome. Then it wouldn't be a coincidence, would it?"

Douglas was about to say, "That's not rational," but stopped himself. Then he said it anyway, because he knew Lise knew what he was thinking.

"Of course it's not rational – rational is to stick with coincidence. The mystery is in wondering what else is happening beneath the surface, if you like. Your little friend wasn't rational, was he?" Lise asked.

"He was to me. I could see him," Douglas replied, laughing. "And I do see what you're getting at. So what are you saying? Are you saying there is no such thing as coincidence?"

"Let's stick with the mystery and say that it *could* be that there is no such thing as coincidence. That way, we can ask some new questions about what's going on, and begin to explore the mystery."

"So where are we with this?" Douglas's left side wanted to put this into context in the logical-rational world. Don't ask me, he said to himself, where would you like to be with it – and immediately realised that he had left himself open on his first question.

"We started out to look at how to effect real change, and saw what you were currently doing. We've since explored the properties of the right / left brain conundrum, leading us, I think, to the conclusion that to change we must spend some time in the magical-mystery world, so as to seek out the bits of the unknown which can be brought back into the left-sided, logical-rational world. Let's take a look at one of your recent strategy meetings."

Lise's mini computer's screen flickered into life once again, and again the *Guardian Angel* boardroom appeared. It was around 3.30pm on a Thursday afternoon and the members of Douglas's senior executive team were assembling round the table. Most looked a bit worn-out and fed-up at having to attend another meeting. David Fleck, Head of Direct Sales – who had only recently been appointed as Executive of this team – turned with a resigned look on his face to Jeremy Dunn, Finance Director and said, "I started at 7.30am this morning and this is the fifth meeting I've attended today."

"This is my third," replied Jeremy. "I've only been

in my office for an hour so far today. Means yet another late night for me. I'll be glad when my holidays come up in six weeks' time. Can't wait."

The other members of the team had now gathered. HR Director Stuart Sutton, Sales and Marketing Director Lydia Simpson, and Operations Director Gordon Fisher. Douglas's deputy, Nick Bell was missing; he was taking his first holiday in nine months.

Douglas was chairing the meeting.

"Do you remember this one?" Lise asked.

"Ah, yes!" replied Douglas. "I do indeed. This was a key strategy meeting to start to frame our planning process for the coming year. Not one of the best, to say the least."

Douglas and Lise both turned back to the screen. Douglas was now talking.

"What we're looking for are as many new ideas as possible, ideas which will separate us from the rest across all areas of the business, but especially in new products. Anyone want to start us off?" he asked.

Everyone in Douglas's team was sitting looking in his direction, but most appeared to be in some kind of trance-like state.

"Hello, is anyone there?" Douglas asked.

"Sorry, Douglas. Where would you like us to start?" Jeremy asked, working hard to look energetic and interested. He had so much going on in his head, thinking about things he had to do that day and other things that were piling up on him, that he found it extremely hard to make space for new thinking. Secretly he thought the best place to start was with a sleep.

"Not so far from the truth," said Lise, turning to Douglas, smiling. Douglas, who didn't understand what she was referring to, returned her smile with a quizzical look. "We'll talk about it in a moment," she said, turning to focus again on the screen.

"Wherever you want," Douglas said in reply to Jeremy's question. "If you guys can't come up with the new ideas, who will?" Douglas continued with a certain caustic tone to his voice.

"What about reviewing where we are currently?" suggested Stuart.

"And where will that take us?" asked Lydia.

Lise faded out the picture and turned once again to Douglas. "Did it get any better?" she asked.

"Not really," he replied. "Most of the time was spent either re-hashing what we'd already done or fighting over who had contributed innovations over the past few years. If I'm perfectly honest, it was a waste of time. Of course, I didn't say that to the team."

"You didn't have to," said Lise, flicking the picture on again.

Jeremy was walking down the corridor away from the meeting, talking with David and Stuart. "What a complete waste of two hours that was," he said, shaking his bald head.

"You're telling me," Stuart responded, shaking his head in unison. "Why do we bother? We always seem to pick a time late in the day and towards the end of the week to try to be creative. And at the end of the day Doug will make up his own mind anyway. We're just going through the motions."

"Nonsense!" Douglas looked as if he was going to attack the screen. "Absolute bloody nonsense! That's not my intention. It's just that they seldom seem to have any decent ideas of their own. Why do they think I had the meeting? I have bigger problems with workload than they do. A cop-out, that's what it is."

Lise wondered what had sparked off so much

frustration and anger in Douglas. "Let's take the emotion out of this and look at the facts in the 'here and now'," suggested Lise, hoping to calm Douglas down.

"Okay, okay, but I do still have a point."

"And so do they."

Douglas still looked frustrated, shaking his head as he continued to look at the blank screen, as if he half hoped his colleagues would re-emerge so that he could have another swipe at them.

"Before we viewed this scenario we had looked at right and left brain activity. Looking at that scene and casting your mind back to the meeting itself, where is it that you would find new ideas, new thinking?" Lise asked.

"On the right side," Douglas replied, almost snapping her head off.

"And how long do you think you spent in right-sided activity during the meeting?"

There was a long silence whilst Douglas wrestled with his thoughts and reflected his new understanding of 'life mirrors'. Lise was happy to sit in silence, giving Douglas the chance to see things for himself.

"I'm not enjoying this at all," Douglas finally said. "Very disconcerting and most uncomfortable."

Lise wondered if he'd noticed. He gave her a look, indicating that he had.

"Again, being completely honest, I'd have to say we didn't spend any time in right-sided activity as you've described it; zero percent to be exact. We spent our entire time on the left, and did so with very little real energy and enthusiasm."

"That may be a bit harsh, though perhaps it is also not so far away from the truth," said Lise. "Do you remember me saying to you that, despite the fact that we humans have an infinite capacity to think, most of us have the same thoughts about ourselves, others and the world around us every day?"

"Yes, I do remember that."

"Just close your eyes for a moment and allow yourself to appreciate what it means to have an infinite capacity to think. What's it like?" Lise asked after a short interval.

"Mind-boggling, when I really think about it. And depressing too, when I take on board the next part about having the same thoughts every day."

"We've already explored why real change is so challenging. So let's look again at this specific situation. Stuart made a good point when he observed the timings of these meetings."

"I usually work on the basis that we get most of the business of the week and that particular day out of the way, so that we can focus on creative thinking. Is this not logical?" Realising what he had just said, Douglas raised his eyebrows and a wry smile spread across his face.

"Let's imagine that the human mind is similar to an emulsion – you know, like a bottle of emulsion – a liquid with lots of bits in it, which when shaken becomes cloudy." Lise went to the flip chart and drew her representation of what she meant.

"The dots represent the solid bits in an emulsion.

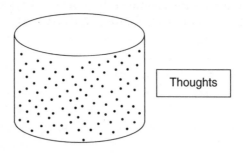

In relation to our mind, they also represent the thoughts that circulate around it on a daily basis. You probably know the feeling yourself. During a normal busy day there seem to be a thousand and one thoughts flying around your head."

Douglas nodded in agreement. He could easily associate with that feeling.

"Imagine your team arriving for that meeting, towards the end of another busy day and week, and imagine what their brain activity would be like," continued Lise. "Looking at my illustration, where would there be room for any new ideas?"

"I get the point," Douglas nodded once again.

"So, what happens when you leave an emulsion to sit for a while?"

"The solids fall to the bottom, leaving a clear space at the top," replied Douglas and a look of recognition spread over his face as he experienced another 'Aah!' moment. "So what you're now going to explain is that we have to allow our thoughts to settle thus leaving some space for creativity, for new thoughts."

"Bravo!" exclaimed Lise, clapping. Once again she was impressed by how quickly Douglas made connections, another area of exploration that could be tackled in the future, she thought.

"Perfect," she continued, "when we allow our brain activity to settle, as you rightly point out, we do give ourselves some clear space to think creatively." Lise went back to the flipchart and drew her container again.

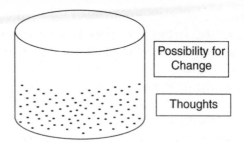

Possibility for Change

Thoughts

"This is obviously a simplistic view of what takes place. But it does provide us with enough understanding to take some corrective action. I bet that if you look back you'll find that you've generated your best ideas about work when you were doing something completely different."

"Yes, I would agree with that," responded Douglas. "And I do remember that Einstein first thought of his theory of relativity whilst lying in the sun daydreaming."

"And, of course, claimed that 'Imagination is more important than knowledge', which in terms of our current discussion could be translated as our right side being more important than our left," added Lise.

"So how does this help me to stimulate creativity in my meetings?" Douglas was keen to find a solution to this problem.

"Let me introduce you to a way that you can personally create space for change, and open up some awareness of your real self in the process. Interested?"

"Well, of course I am. That's why we're here, isn't it?"

"Okay, here goes. Remember our sitting exercise?" asked Lise.

Douglas adjusted his sitting position, so that his

backside was pushed into the back of the seat, his sacrum supporting his back, his feet flat on the ground and his hands sitting on the front of this thighs.

"I've actually found I'm sitting this way more often, and find it more comfortable now," commented Douglas, looking rather pleased with himself.

"I know, I've noticed," Lise said, smiling back. "Well done."

"I am surprised that something which felt so unnatural and uncomfortable now feels good. I even find myself looking quite critically at others when they sit unproductively."

Lise smiled again without commenting and was pleased that Douglas was moving on as well as he was, and now even using new language.

"I will describe the process to you before we actually experience it so that you can clarify anything you're not sure of," she said. "As you close your eyes at the start of the process you will take two deep breaths. As you breathe in, imagine you're breathing in relaxation or 'letting go'. As you breathe out, breathe out any tension or need to 'hold on'. Then I will ask you to imagine that I can pour a special relaxation fluid into you through the top of your head. As it flows down through you it will help to soften any areas which you may be holding."

"For example?" Douglas asked.

"Your jaw, neck, shoulders, back, and so on. You'll soon find out as we progress with the activity. When you are physically relaxed, I will ask you to become aware of your breathing – just noticing where the breath comes in and where it goes out. It's not a special breathing technique, it's simply a matter of noticing something that you do unconsciously every moment of every day. What will happen is you will begin to become aware of your thoughts. In fact, sometimes you will be well into a stream of thoughts before you realise you are thinking. When you do become conscious of this, imagine you can stick a label on your thoughts: a 'THINKING' label, like a Royal Mail 'HANDLE WITH CARE' label. Then send them on their way, and come back to noticing your breathing."

"You mean I have to try to shut out my thoughts?" asked Douglas.

"Definitely not," replied Lise. "Thinking is a normal function of being human. Trying not to have thoughts is, after all, a thought in itself. What we are aiming to do is to acknowledge our thoughts and then let them go, coming back to the 'here and now' of our breathing. And, when we practise this regularly, we will experience moments of 'no thoughts' – what some call 'being in the gap' between thoughts. Here is the space that we talked about earlier. Unfortunately it is almost impossible to be conscious of that state, because every time we realise we are not thinking, we're actually having another thought!"

Douglas and Lise both laughed at that.

"How long will we do this for?" Douglas asked.

"Ideally for twenty minutes; but we'll make it just ten minutes for our first attempt. Ready?"

Douglas nodded, took his two deep breaths and closed his eyes. Lise talked him through the physical relaxation phase with the special relaxing fluid. Softening the skin on his forehead, his face, his eye sockets, his jaw, down through his neck, his shoulders and into his lower back, down his chest and arms and softening his fingers, and then into his legs, knees, calves and finally his feet and toes. After this

Lise talked him through his awareness of his breathing and then let him practise for almost ten minutes without instruction as she joined in. When the ten minutes were up, they opened their eyes and sat quietly for a couple of minutes.

"So, what relevance does this have to discussion in our meetings?" Douglas was very good at wanting to make the connection between right and left side activities. "Are you suggesting we do this before every meeting?"

"It's a possibility," Lise responded. "Or perhaps introduce what I call a 'quiet five' – asking people to sit with their eyes closed for five minutes, noticing their own relaxation and then their breathing, letting the 'dust' of the day and week settle before opening up to new possibilities."

"And you reckon this will help us to become more creative?"

"Yes I do. You can also implement other ideas to establish a more creative environment."

"In what way?" Douglas was keen to get down to the specifics.

"Well, if we think back to that change programme session we watched a little while ago, we could get some clues," replied Lise, offering Douglas the opportunity to supply some answers himself.

Slightly frustrated at not being told the answers, Douglas replied, "You mean a less formal atmosphere?"

"Yes, that would be good. For example?" Lise mirrored Douglas's questioning style.

"Beyond dressing down into less formal clothes, I'm not sure there's anything else we could do."

"Dressing less formally would certainly help for these types of meetings. And if you were to be able to find something else to do, what would it be?" Lise was pleased with how she had worded this to further encourage Douglas to explore his own imagination.

"Being really radical, we could do away with the table we sit around – even the chairs we sit on. How about bringing in some cushions?" Douglas was getting into full flow. "We could made the whole process more fun."

"More playful?" Lise suggested.

"Yes. Not sure how to, but I'm sure there is a way."

"Music is a possibility," suggested Lise. "And less use of PowerPoint materials and overheads, and more participation from all concerned. There are lots of ways to get people more involved."

"So, after all this fun, where do we go?" Douglas was back on the left.

"Then it's time to move back to the left and work out ways of implementing the ideas, including their feasibility," Lise responded.

"Hmmm, sounds interesting." Douglas closed his eyes as he imagined what such a meeting would look like.

"No need to imagine," said Lise, interrupting Douglas's daydreaming. "Take a look."

Again Lise's mini computer's screen lit up and the members of the executive team reappeared. Music was playing as they came into the room; all were casually dressed and looking much more energetic and enthusiastic. Lise and Douglas watched as they completed a 'quiet five' sitting on their cushions, followed by a participation process which resulted in numerous new ideas emerging, some of which were only feasible in the long-term and others which could be implemented within months.

As Lise turned the screen off again, Douglas

turned to her and nodded his approval. She realised that her three days were almost up and there was still much to do. She still had to take him through dialoguing, the language of success, built-in inefficiencies and probably a few more issues besides.

Chapter Sixteen

Take Over?

"Great doubt, great awakening,
Little doubt, little awakening,
No doubt, no awakening."

Zen proverb

'G UARDIAN ANGEL UP FOR GRABS' AND 'ANGEL'S wings to be clipped' were two of the headlines which greeted Douglas as he scanned the financial sections of the papers in his office. A month had passed since Douglas had spent his three days with Lise. Much had happened since, most of it having been in the pipeline for some time.

Douglas had been in discussions for a long period with a potential suitor – one of the major banks. *Guardian Angel* would become a division of the bank, whilst still retaining its identity. This was becoming more and more common in the financial sector, with mutual companies such as Scottish Widows, Scottish Mutual and Scottish Provident all being swallowed up in much the same way. The argument for it had been well worked. The way ahead was to de-mutu-alise and become a Plc, or part of a Plc, with access to greater levels of investment, economies of scale, shared overheads, and so on. It all made sound economic sense and, of course, with the globalisation of business it made sense to become a world player for bigger stakes.

The downside was that inevitably people would lose their jobs, the organisation would become even less personal and the opportunities for politicking, pursuing hidden agendas and games-playing would increase exponentially.

Just as he was getting to grips with his own personal change process, and even seeing signs of change in others in *Guardian Angel*, Douglas was being confronted with giving all this up and becoming part of what now looked like a very reactionary, old-fashioned company. As one might expect, the bank was very hierarchical – as *Guardian Angel* had been, but Douglas had begun the process to change that. The bank's employees were highly status-conscious, with title and position a matter of great importance, and very ego-driven. These were all things that had been exposed to Douglas through Lise, and they were all things that he wished to change at *Guardian Angel*. It was almost unbelievable that just a month earlier none of this would have been of any real importance to Douglas. Although he would no longer be Chief Executive of a stand-alone company, he would have an increased salary, would be vice-president of a major corporation (and who knows what else? Douglas used to think) and be more involved in global financial affairs. It had all seemed so logical to him then. Now he wasn't so sure.

Douglas had been experiencing these feelings of uncertainty for some time and had attempted to contact Lise to talk them through with her. He had been stunned to find that she had left the company the week after they had completed their work. Although their agreement had been to work together for three days, it had been Douglas's intention to work with her on a regular basis in the future. He had immediately investigated her speedy departure, attempting to find out where she'd gone. She had been on the pay roll, which he hadn't been certain of at one time. People said she always seemed to flit in and out, producing excellent work without ever getting involved in any of the normal office politics. Douglas spoke to a few people who confirmed that Lise did seem to have a magical energy around her. Only people who had worked closely with her seemed to know her, whilst others in Marketing had never heard of her or even seen her. She had left no forwarding address and, although he had followed up a few lines of inquiry, he'd been unable to make contact with her.

But Lise's presence could still be felt, Douglas thought, smiling as he looked out of his seventh-storey window. Had they actually happened, these amazing experiences? It was just unbelievable. He ran though a few in his mind. The runaway carriage, the plane, the football team, the well-trodden path, all amazing learning experiences and all still very much part of his new consciousness. One of the challenges Douglas had to deal with was all the inappropriate behaviour and general level of unconsciousness he now noticed around him. He was learning, slowly, to let go of the need to judge people on what he saw. A very difficult task in itself, he thought.

One of the major influences behind Douglas's change of heart was the meeting he had had three weeks ago with the bank's board and the respective lawyers, accountants and other advisers to frame-up the take-over deal. He would rather it were seen as a merger, but that was a fanciful thought since the bank's assets were ten times those of *Guardian Angel*'s.

Douglas closed his eyes and thought back to that life-changing meeting once again.

The Chairman, James Orr-Smith was starting the meeting off in his usual very formal manner. The boardroom they were using was very grand. In the centre of the room stood a huge, polished oak table with a rosewood inlay around its edge. It could easily seat up to forty people. From the ceiling hung three chandeliers, and matching wall lights were dotted around the room, alternating with portraits of various chairmen of the bank, some of which were 200 years old.

"Thank you for being so punctual and allowing us to get started on time," said Orr-Smith. In his sixties, Orr-Smith retained a plentiful head of hair, all of which had turned completely white. His eyebrows, however, had remained dark and looked like two black bushes that had sprouted up above his eyes. He wore the ubiquitous half-moon spectacles, over which he peered in time-honoured fashion. After spending five years in the army, reaching the rank of Major, Orr-Smith had gone straight into a City investment bank and pursued a most successful career, which culminated in his running an international banking empire. He had retired three years ago and held, apart from his present role, another two non-executive positions in major companies.

"Firstly, welcome to Douglas, who joins us today to begin the formal discussions about *Guardian Angel* becoming part of our company."

Douglas almost winced as he recalled the moment.

He now felt that he was giving away his life's work, having been seduced by the apparent benefits this would bring.

"This will be a long meeting I suspect, so avoid any unnecessary complications or diversions..." continued Orr-Smith.

Recalling the meeting in his mind, Douglas remembered the whole experience as being unconnected in any human sense. For example, almost no one had made eye contact with anyone else when they spoke, and people had interrupted each other to make their own point. All sorts of inappropriate behaviour were on display, none of which, Douglas now realised, he would have noticed before his meetings with Lise. He was seriously questioning whether he could now go ahead with the deal or whether it would be possible for him to pull out.

Chapter Seventeen

Re-Connecting

*"Nothing perfect or close to perfect can stay that way
without a tremendous effort spent in maintenance."*
Malidoma Patrice Some

DOUGLAS'S FINAL SESSION WITH LISE HAD PLAYED A major part in his increased consciousness during the take-over negotiations, not least because one of the scenarios she had shown him was very similar to the board meeting he had just been thinking about. This scenario had been a meeting of the senior managers in Sales and Marketing, chaired by Lydia Simpson.

"Looking at the next six months, it's imperative that we are able to generate new sales from our existing customers at the same time as we penetrate the markets and customers of our competitors. As well as offering new products, we need to capture the imagination of our customers through innovative marketing," said Lydia, who was getting into full flow when Douglas and Lise started viewing.

"I think we should start by reviewing the marketing agencies we're using. I'm not sure we're getting the best deal or that they are the most creative available," said Mike Duncan. He had held this view for some time and had expressed it many times before.

Lydia didn't agree and believed Mike simply had some kind of hang-up about the agencies they used. "Look Mike, I hear what you're saying, but surely we've been through this one enough before. I don't see how looking at it again will make any difference." Lydia was now leaning back in her seat with a resigned look on her face.

"What's the point of having a meeting if we can't raise our concerns?" Mike's voice displayed signs of both anger and frustration. He believed that Lydia stuck with the agencies in question because they had been good pals for many years.

"But we've been around the houses on this one so many times, it only means going over the same ground again," responded Lydia, looking around the table for some indication of the mood of the others. "What do the rest of you think? Do we look at this again? Or do we move on?"

Lydia raised her eyebrows, pursed her lips and scanned the faces of her colleagues. All nodded in agreement. indicating that they too wanted to move on. Mike's shoulders dropped a little and he looked a bit miffed. Douglas wondered if he would have noticed this three days ago. He would probably have been applauding Lydia for her apparent strength of character.

"I see Mike's point to some extent, but I agree that we should move on to other matters," said Jane Williamson, who took it upon herself to speak on behalf of the others.

"So how do you suggest we be more creative with our marketing if we stay with the same agency?" Mike wasn't letting it go.

"Let it go, Mike. It's pretty obvious that we're not going anywhere with this, isn't it?" asked David Fleck.

"That may be your view, David," Mike replied. "But I'd like that question answered first." He sat back and looked round.

"As David has just said, we need to move on, Mike. Surely you can see that." Lydia was looking pretty frustrated by now. "And David, you normally have some fresh ideas for us; got anything you'd like to put forward?"

David noticed that her look was one of expectation. In other words, 'You'd better have something for us to get Mike off my back' was the hidden message.

"Nothing specific at the moment," David had to admit. "I had thought we'd be able to stimulate some new ideas at this meeting." He said this in the hope that it would save him.

"Yes, but you were supposed to come with some idea of where we were going." Lydia had raised the pitch of her voice.

"Sorry, Lydia, I was busy finishing that report for you on our performance over the last three months."

Lydia flushed with anger.

"Look," Lydia said, "if we all focus our attention on the task in hand and try to generate some new ideas, then we might just be able to surprise Douglas with our results over the next six months."

"I think we've seen enough," Lise said, turning off the film. "What did you think?" She turned and looked at Douglas. She had an almost saintly air about her, he thought, as she looked at him, her eyes penetrating yet soft and kind.

"There seemed to be very little appreciation of people's point of view. Lydia seemed to have her own agenda set before the meeting even started and she wasn't really interested in hearing other points of view," said Douglas, looking to Lise for confirmation of his assessment.

"Yes, I agree. And as we've observed in other meetings, there was a lot of unproductive behaviour."

"And, of course, they could have created a more stimulating environment if they had wanted the creativity to flow," added Douglas. Lise was secretly amazed at the change in Douglas's perception over such a short period of time. If he was able to get a critical mass of people in the business to move with him, he would really transform this company, she thought.

"Thanks," Douglas smiled at Lise. "What a great thought."

"Wow, you have moved!" Lise exclaimed. "One of the challenges, which you've often experienced, is how to really tap into the true potential of your people. You saw quite clearly in that last clip, as you have done in many of the previous ones, that people were not freely sharing their energy. Nor were they all focused on achieving the best possible outcome for all concerned."

"But surely we can't please everyone all the time by incorporating each person's ideas into every solution we come up with?"

"Yes, you're right. It won't be possible to incorporate everyone's contribution every time, and you have provided me with an excellent example of what we want to avoid whilst in dialogue."

Douglas waited in expectation of her explanation. "Later," she said. "I'd like to start by exploring the skills of dialoguing and incorporate your own example within this context."

Douglas nodded his approval. He trusted Lise to lead him through what he needed to know.

"Firstly, dialoguing is different from discussion – it has no pre-determined framework, no specific outcome in mind."

"Does that not lead to meetings simply going off on tangents without sticking to the point?" Douglas asked.

"Martin Buber, the philosopher, described this concept of dialoguing in 1914 as a type of exchange amongst people where there is a true turning to each other and where people appreciate one another as genuine human beings rather than as human 'doings' or, in organisations, as a resource.

"In everyday language [dialoguing] provides the stage upon which people can truly be heard and appreciated – it gives people the freedom to express their true thoughts and feelings. So, in this context, people will not require to have their ideas incorporated into every solution as long as they feel that they have been listened to and respected. Each person's map of the world is different. We've already seen this. The challenge is to accept that although it may not be the most productive or resourceful one, it is still that person's current perception and it should be respected. Not to do so will often lead to that individual withdrawing their commitment and energy from the solution. You don't really think Mike will be keen to support Lydia's solution in the scenario we've just seen, do you?" asked Lise.

"Far from it," Douglas responded, nodding in agreement. "It's more likely he will look forward to sabotaging the solution."

"Most probably," Lise sighed. "Managers often boast that they get people to agree to the solution they wanted by making it seem as though they'd thought of it themselves."

"Yes. Been there, done that." Douglas was shaking his head in apparent disapproval of his actions.

"That's not perhaps as bad as it may seem to you – where business circumstances or legal constraints prevail, there may only be a limited solution possible. It may be better, however, to share that with the team at the outset."

Lise walked across the room to the flipchart, and drew a square in the middle of the page, followed by a series of smaller boxes inside the square:

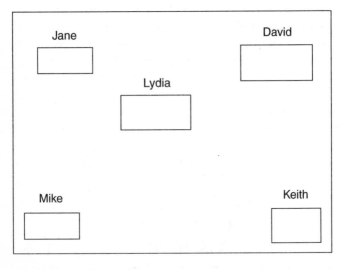

"Let's imagine that the large square represents the potential solution to a problem. In other words, the square incorporates all the possibilities that could be available to us. Because each person will only have a limited view of the possibilities available the small boxes represent their 'take' on the issue."

"Their map?" Douglas asked.

"Yes, their map. So, if I put the names of some of the people in the Sales and Marketing team above each box, you can see that each person, including Lydia, has only a limited view of the potential solutions."

"Caused by the filters we talked about the other day?" Douglas was pleased at how he had integrated his learning from the past three days.

"Spot on!" Lise replied. "So, again in simple terms, the choice we have now is to either fight to prove that our map is the best – or the only one. Or we can find a way of sharing our maps more productively." Lise then coloured in a part of each of four of the five boxes. "By dialoguing effectively a bit of each person's map can become part of a more expansive solution." Lise completed the diagram.

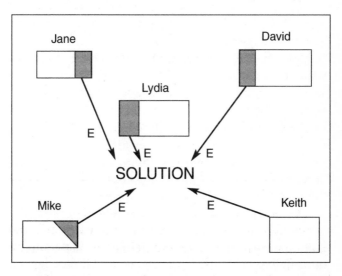

"The arrows and the 'Es' represent each individual's energy focused towards the agreed solution," explained Lise.

"What about Keith?" Douglas asked.

"Although his map, and possibly other's, don't directly contribute to the solution, if he has been listened to and respected, then he would happily have directed his energy to making the solution work."

"So, what does effective dialoguing look like, sound like, and feel like?" Douglas was keen to get an insight into some of the specific skills. He noticed again his desire to get to the logical-rational issues, and smiled to himself.

"You'll have noticed in a number of our scenarios how some people have frequently interrupted others in mid-flow, in order to make their own point or to indicate to the other person that the view they have just expressed is wrong and that their view is the right one."

"I not only noticed it, I've done it myself often enough. Especially when people just don't seem to be able to grasp what we've been discussing."

Lise fell silent once again to allow Douglas to deal with what he had said. "Most people do this," she said eventually. "Especially when they're passionate about something. But what this does is at least twofold. Firstly, you miss the whole 'message' from the other person, and secondly the 'message' they receive from you is that you're not listening and you don't respect their views or appreciate their contributions. In other words, you discount them."

Douglas indicated that he understood.

"As a result, it's likely that they start to withdraw their energy. Hence you lose the potential they have to contribute."

Douglas could recall nasty meetings in which he had steam-rollered his ideas through, discounting the views of others as irrelevant, simplistic or poorly articulated. He could now quite easily imagine the subsequent behaviour of his team after those meetings, and could see further evidence of why the company hadn't developed the way he had wanted it to.

Lise was now enjoying herself at the flipchart. She drew her next illustration:

"You can see that I've drawn two people, at least my representation of two people," Lise said, smiling. "One is yourself, and the other is someone in your team – you can choose whoever it is. Again you will see that I've written 'map' above each person's head, representing their take on a specific issue. The river between represents the potential gulf between each person's map.

"Makes sense," Douglas muttered quietly to himself.

"To sell someone a new idea, or persuade him or her to at least have a look at a different perspective, you need to get them across the river. The size of the gulf between your maps will determine how much work you will have to do. What do you reckon the traditional method would be to get someone to go along with your idea?" Lise asked Douglas.

"I'd just tell them!" Douglas replied.

"And what was your thinking behind your answer?" said Lise, continuing her questioning.

"It's quick and to the point."

"And successful?"

"Most probably not. I can now see that people would resist actually coming across the river. They may pretend to go along with me whilst remaining where they are."

"Any other better ideas to get them across?"

"A bridge would be useful; or I could always use a boat!" Douglas laughed.

"We'll go with the bridge for now. Whose responsibility would it be to build the bridge?"

"If it's me doing the persuading, it would be mine, I guess".

"Any ideas on how to build the bridge?"

"Going from what we looked at earlier, listening to what the other person is saying would be a good start."

"The perfect start, in fact! And what next?"

"Demonstrate that you have listened?" Douglas was looking for confirmation from Lise.

"Again, perfect. The skill we use here is the skill of 'pacing'. You've probably heard of pacing in athletics: you know, when one athlete runs at the pace another one wants to race at, so as to help them set a new record. We have a variety of tactics available in pacing, but for now we will concentrate on one key tactic. How, for example, could you let the other person know that you have listened to them?"

This is a bit like Question Time, Douglas thought. "I suppose I could repeat back to them roughly what they said to me," he suggested.

"Wow. Right first time, again." As Lise was showing her delight, Douglas wondered what Bett was making of all the whooping and laughter going on.

"Take a look again at the meeting we've just seen – I'll move it around a bit to focus on the relevant parts. Notice if you hear any discounts or non-pacing activity." Lise ran through the film again, stopping at key moments.

"Hear anything?" Lise asked, turning to Douglas after switching off the film.

"I noticed Lydia used 'but' a lot, sometimes prefaced with that wonderful line, 'I hear what you're saying'," replied Douglas.

"'But' is a great word if you really want to discount people's views, especially when it's used to interrupt someone. The word has a huge impact for us when dialoguing, because it has the effect of erasing what has just been said before. So even if you have paced the other person effectively by repeating or paraphrasing what they've just said, the 'but' will remove this. It's as if the first part hasn't been said; and it focuses the other person's attention on what comes next."

"Which is usually our own map!" Douglas exclaimed.

"Yes, correct again, which means that the other person received only *your* connection to *your own* point of view. And when you use a word like 'surely' or 'obviously' you add to the impact. You suggest that your map is 'surely' right and theirs is wrong, just as you did with me a little while ago," said Lise.

Douglas looked over his glasses at her with a quizzical look. Then he nodded and smiled. "Ah, yes, I remember. That was the bit you told me we'd come back to later. So, do I use 'however' instead of 'but' to get a better result?" he asked.

"'However' unfortunately has the same effect as 'but', although slightly less so," replied Lise "So it's also better to also avoid 'however' in this context

"Which context are we talking about?" Douglas was keen to clarify this, as Lise was apparently suggesting that he stop using words he'd been using all his life.

"We're talking about when we want to make sure that people receive both parts of our message. Which is firstly, that we've heard what they said and secondly, that they receive our interpretation of the issue. It doesn't mean you have to stop using these words in all contexts."

"So, what will I replace 'but' and 'however' with?"

"With 'and'," said Lise with an impish grin on her face.

"'And'!" Douglas exclaimed. "That doesn't sound right at all!"

"It won't sound right to you to begin with, and you will feel uncomfortable using it. And," Lise continued, emphasising her use of the word, "when you stay conscious and use it over time it will become your new 'habit'. You've already agreed that when you change something you're used to doing you will feel uncomfortable for a time."

"So much we do unconsciously is unproductive – it's amazing," Douglas responded. "The vast majority of people probably spend their whole lives without waking up to what's stopping them achieving what they really want.".

Lise was interested that Douglas had made such a leap in his thinking, from looking at specific skills to general levels of consciousness. Then she remembered the Eastern philosophers and their saying that, when the time is right, the simple observation of a leaf floating safely to the ground will be enough to awaken a person. For others, the whole forest can fall down without it having any impact on them. Douglas's observation was further indication of the timeliness of his awakening.

"The normal course of events in meetings is for separation to take place rather than connection or a real 'coming together' – which is the real aim of meeting in the first place." Lise strongly emphasised the word 'meeting'. "When people learn to relax their need to defend their apparent truth – their map – and to stop attacking others, they really begin to tap into the true potential of themselves as a team. People talk a lot about 'team spirit' without really realising what they're talking about. How would you describe 'spirit' in the context of teams?" Lise asked Douglas, putting him on the spot. It was something he'd never really thought about.

"I've certainly used the term many times without really thinking of its significance. If 'spirit' is the non-material element of a human being, then 'team spirit' must be the non-material element which makes a team a team."

Douglas looked pleased with himself. It sounded pretty good to him.

"I'm impressed," Lise said, looking delighted. "And how many teams have you been involved with who paid attention to the non-material aspect of their activity – the spiritual element which keeps them bound as a team?"

"Apart from those participating in drunken nights out or occasional 'away days', which also involve an excess of alcohol, none that I know of."

"We've digressed slightly from what we began to look at this session, although it is all connected. We can follow up on this again at the end when we look at the concept of built-in inefficiencies. Let's finish off our session on pacing and what I call the language of success."

'Built-in inefficiencies'? Douglas wondered what in heaven's name they were. Lise smiled at him.

"Okay, okay, I've had my eyes well and truly opened on so many occasions, I trust you to continue to do so." Douglas held both hands up towards Lise as if to surrender to her greater knowledge.

"Come," she said to Douglas, "remember the football team?"

How could I forget? Douglas wondered.

Lise opened the door and once again she and Douglas were in another world, back in the football dressing room that had made such an impression on Douglas the first time he saw it.

"We'll only stay very briefly this time," whispered Lise, again wondering why she had bothered. The manager was speaking to his team, again trying to sound very confident and sure of what he was saying.

"If you guys go out there today and try your best, you might pull off a victory." The manager was very focused as he looked menacingly at every member of the team.

"We've seen enough," said Lise, turning to leave.

"So soon?" asked Douglas. "I enjoy these little trips." As he followed Lise back into his office, Douglas thought how blasé he now was about stepping out of his office, becoming invisible and being transported to unusual places.

"What did you get from that?" Lise asked Douglas.

"Sounded as if he really wanted them to win, but there was something about his speech that wasn't really convincing. It was almost de-motivating."

Lise flicked her film back on again to watch the meeting they'd already seen twice before.

"Listen," she said.

Lydia was speaking.

"Look," she said, "if we all focus our attention on the task in hand and try to generate some new ideas, we might just be able to surprise Douglas with our results over the next six months."

"Sound familiar?" Lise asked, turning the film off again.

"Very similar to what the football manager said. Came across again as unconvincing and potentially de-motivating."

"In each case they used three words which give the team members an opt-out clause! They both used 'if', 'try' and 'might'. 'If' is very much an either / or. 'Try' is very unconvincing – have you ever heard someone say 'I'll try and make it?' You just know that they won't. And 'might' has no conviction at all."

"The team members are really receiving a cop-out from their manager?" Douglas wouldn't normally use a term such as cop-out and it grated a bit as he heard himself say it.

"They are indeed," said Lise, nodding.

"There is no commitment and certainly no confidence inherent in those words. If I was going to change that I'd replace 'if' with 'when', 'try' with 'do' and 'might' with 'will'." Douglas had gone into free flow.

"Well done! I'm becoming superfluous to this process."

Not so, thought Douglas, you are simply skilfully giving me the opportunity to work things out for myself.

"So the football manager would be better saying to his team," Douglas continued, enjoying his moment of glory, "'When you guys go out there today, and do the things you know you can do, you will win this game.' Sounds good, and a bit risky?" Douglas was grinning and hoping Lise would notice his use of 'and'.

"Great language pattern," she said, leaning forward and tapping the outside of his knee in approval. It was the first time, Douglas noted, that they had made any contact other than shake hands. Not that he had any thoughts in that direction, he just noticed that he felt well supported by her subtle use of touch.

"You're right. There is more risk in using that language than with the first pattern. It's a bit like the golfer and the four-foot putt. An amateur doesn't want to expect to hole it just in case he should miss it, which inevitably means he does miss the putt. A professional, on the other hand, expects to hole a four-foot putt and learns to deal with the times he doesn't. The first language pattern equates to providing a large psychological safety net in case things don't work out; the second pattern indicates a clear intention and commitment towards the desired outcome. Again, it's very powerful, and it's amazing how few people are consciously aware of this."

Douglas had noticed that since starting his work with Lise he observed more than he ever had before, both in his own language and behaviour and in those of others. He found it extremely difficult at times to stop himself from pointing out these observations to the people around him. This had certainly been a challenge for his wife Pat, who'd taken the full force of his newfound awareness.

"Before I forget, Lise, can you explain what you meant by built-in inefficiencies? Sit sounds like such a weird concept in the age of Total Quality Management – right first time and all the rest."

"In his book, Secrets of the Talking Jaguar, Martin Pretchel talks about built-in inefficiencies in reference to the true indigenous communities of Guatemala," Lise explained. "These communities remained close-ly-knit because the people made sure that what they created was never so efficient that it would not need 'repairing' on a regular basis."

"Interesting, but – oops – and can you give me some specifics?" Douglas asked.

"That's just what I was about to do," continued Lise. "One example is that the communities didn't build their houses to last too long because, when they began to fall down, or indeed did fall down, an opportunity was presented for people to come together to rebuild them. And, in so doing, they also 'rebuilt' their communities. The people recognised their need to re-new, re-connect and re-energise their communities on a regular basis, so they used any breakdown opportunity to do this. Rather than leave this to chance, they built these opportunities into the way they lived."

"Wouldn't go down too well in a modern manage-ment textbook," Douglas replied. "I wonder what the gurus of Business Process Re-engineering would make of it all?" Douglas grinned and winced inside at the sound of the term, which he once thought was the answer to business success. Lise was switching the film on again; Douglas had an idea of what may be about to be shown. He was not wrong.

The scene was the *Guardian Angel* boardroom. Douglas was once again chairing his executive management team meeting.

"The only way to real success is through greater levels of efficiency. Efficiency, efficiency, efficiency should be our company mantra." Douglas was in a serious mood as he delivered this business sermon. "In the business environment we operate in, we cannot afford mistakes. Mistakes cost us money and reputation. We must aim for a 'right first time' mentality and refuse to tolerate anything less. We must only innovate if it leads to success." Douglas scanned his team's faces for their reaction. Watching this replay he noticed that almost everyone looked downwards as he addressed them, and no one had disputed these strong sentiments.

Lise turned the film off again, stood up and headed for the door.

We're off again, Douglas thought to himself.

Douglas and Lise headed down in the special lift they'd used before. "Where to this time?" Douglas asked in eager anticipation as the lift descended.

"The staff restaurant again," replied Lise, as she slipped out of the lift. "Over here." Lise directed Douglas to a table with three people sitting around it and a couple of spare seats. "We'll use these for now," said Lise, sitting down on one of the empty seats.

Douglas sat down beside Lise. It was certainly a 'high' table in terms of company status. Sitting around in serious and solemn discussion were Finance Director Jeremy Dunn, Operations Director Gordon Simpson and HR Director Stuart Sutton.

"What a cock-up she's made now," said Gordon,

holding court.

"What do you mean?" Stuart asked.

"It was Lydia's idea to appoint David Fleck as Head of Direct Sales. Now look what's happened." Gordon was in a belligerent, judgmental mood. "Two basic errors and our new with profits bond has fallen flat on its face."

"My advice would be to steer well clear of that scene," chipped in Jeremy.

"Exactly. Let them stew in their own juice." Stuart was warming to the discussion. "They're always so full of themselves, as if the whole company revolves around marketing."

Douglas glanced at Lise and shook his head in acknowledgement of the connections he was making.

"And you can count on them to disappear if any of us has a problem," Gordon added, noticing only fleetingly that most people are on their own when an error occurs.

"Let's get back." Lise turned and nudged Douglas who was again looking shell- shocked on discovering what was actually happening within his beloved company. "We've still some more to do before we finish today," she whispered to him as they headed back for the lift.

"I can see how the drive for efficiency at all costs can lead to separation rather pulling the team together. Rather than build what we talked about earlier – team spirit – we achieve fragmentation." Douglas was back in his office pacing up and down by the window.

"Unfortunately this appears to be the case. There seems to be very little or no sense of spirit or community compared with the example given by Martin Pretchel, where errors would be seen as the ideal

opportunity to build communities. Perhaps something to build into your organisation of the future,"
added Lise, trying to pull Douglas out of the trance
he appeared to be in.

"Yes, yes, definitely," he responded. "Sorry, I've
got a lot of stuff going through my mind right now."

Chapter Eighteen

Rethink?

"Time is a powerful river of passing events; no sooner is one thing brought to sight than it is swept away and another takes its place – and this, too will be swept away."

Marcus Aurelius

TARA WAS BUZZING ABOUT AS USUAL, NOSE CLOSE TO the ground, picking up and snapping small sticks in her mouth and occasionally bringing back a larger one for Douglas, looking for all the world like a conqueror who had vanquished a foe. Douglas took a stick from her mouth. Occasionally Tara held on and played tug-of-war, but this time she let him have it. Douglas threw the stick to the edge of the stream and Tara took off in hot pursuit, her tail circling frantically to slow her down and stop herself from careering into the water.

Douglas smiled. As always, it was Tara who managed to help him reconnect with the simpler moments in life. Increased salaries, pensions, long-term investments and take-overs were not part of Tara's world. No matter what decisions he made, she would remain his faithful, fun-filled friend.

Reflecting on his newfound consciousness, Douglas was amazed at both what he now saw and at what he had previously missed when he'd been asleep. A little over a month ago his main concern was how to negotiate this take-over to the benefit of himself and his members. Douglas had felt he had done all he could to take *Guardian Angel* forward in his five years as Chief Executive, and he had believed that the only way to do it was to become part of a bigger entity. It was the way the financial world was going. It was inevitable; he had thought, and why fight the inevitable?

The currently accepted wisdom of the business world was that *Guardian Angel*, and similar-sized organisations, simply were not big enough to survive independently. But was this really true, or was it just an example of mass hypnosis? What would happen, Douglas wondered, if *Guardian Angel* did go it alone?

Since meeting Lise, Douglas had begun to see the world differently. He remembered his pride at becoming Chief Executive at 42 years of age, and recalled his aim of creating a different business: one that was both very successful in the market place, and so good to work for that people would queue up to join it. In a sense, Douglas had almost achieved his first aim, although he realised that, had he been really successful, he might not have needed to sell the company. With the insights Lise had given him, Douglas could see that he had certainly *not* succeeded in achieving his second goal, and that he would have little opportunity to do so in an enlarged, merged organisation. Once that happened he would be almost totally consumed by strategic issues, and he would be working with a global perspective which he was simply not used to. On the one hand this would be a great challenge, and on the other it would be a great shame, since in this new scenario his awakened sense of what was possible would hardly be used.

As he walked, Douglas also noticed that his consciousness of his world around him had been heightened by his experience with Lise. The shape of the trees, the subtle changes of colour in the leaves, the water in the stream running up and around blue stone. Douglas wondered how long this process had been going on, the water shaping and polishing the stone so that it glistened in the evening sunlight.

Over the past month, as he had already observed more than once, Douglas had had a really productive effect on those around him. He had worked hard to put into practice the skills and awareness he had been introduced to, and he had seen some very promising results, not least from the creativity his executive team was beginning to display. They also seemed willing to set themselves more challenging goals, and were more able to focus their teams' energy in the process of achieving them. This thought reminded Douglas of one of his final sessions with Lise.

"Do you know one of the reasons why many businesses and individuals fail to achieve the outcomes they desire?" Lise had asked him.

Douglas had shrugged his shoulders in response.

"Their obsession with the outcome," said Lise, answering her own question. "When people become attached to the outcome they invite fear, doubt and anxiety into the equation and allow themselves to sabotage the 'process'." Lise emphasised this word. "And, if they do eventually achieve their outcome, it is at what expense? The journey towards it has been so fraught that the thought of setting out once again to achieve more is often less than exciting."

"This cuts across most of what is written these days by the management and self-development gurus," said Douglas. "I've come across a number who suggest we revisit our goals – or outcomes, as you call them – on a daily basis. That surely cuts across what you're saying; or I would be better saying, it *appears to me* that it cuts across what you're saying?" Douglas did not comment on his self-correction, it was becoming part of his everyday life.

"My understanding of how we get our lives to work for us, including achieving the outcomes we want, is firstly to be clear about our 'intention'," Lise said, writing this word in large print on the flipchart. "Our intention is, in effect, our outcome – what we wish to achieve. When we have a clear intention we can let go our need to be attached to it and focus our 'attention' on the process."

Lise returned to the flipchart and wrote:

INTENTION

↓

ATTENTION

"And when our intention is clear, and contains both our commitment and certainty," Lise continued, "then our mind acts like a laser beam, allowing us to pay attention to what we need to achieve our desired outcome."

Lise reached into her bag and took out a set of juggling balls. Douglas's initial reaction was, what now? Was this a bit of his old thinking creeping back? Douglas smiled and gave himself permission to relax and let the process happen.

"Watch!" Lise exclaimed, catching Douglas's attention. She started juggling the three coloured balls with professional ease. "What do you think?" she asked, stopping for a moment.

"Brilliant!" Douglas replied, noticing how something so relatively simple could impress him so much. Indeed, he was surprised that something so playful could excite him. "Not sure if I could learn to do it though."

"I'm sure you could when you decided you wanted to. Not now though – maybe later or another time."

Douglas felt a twinge of disappointment, but realised Lise had introduced this for reasons other than to teach him to juggle.

"Watch again, only this time look and tell me what I'm focusing on – throwing the balls, or catching them?"

Douglas watched intently as Lise started juggling again. "What do you think?" she asked, this time continuing to juggle.

"Looks to me as if you're focusing on throwing the balls," Douglas replied.

"Sure?" Lise asked, continuing to juggle, varying the height and angle of throw.

"Definitely!" Douglas was laughing at her ability to manipulate the balls.

"You're right. Look what happens when I focus on catching," said Lise. As she started looking at her hands the balls fell to the ground. "So, what is the ultimate outcome in juggling?" Lise asked, bending down to pick up the juggling balls.

"To be able to catch the balls as they come down, so that they can be thrown back up."

"So, catching is the outcome."

"And throwing is the process," added Douglas before Lise had the chance to say it.

"Exactly! And what do you think is the biggest fear for people beginning to learn to juggle?" asked Lise.

"Dropping the balls," Douglas replied.

"So what do you think beginners focus on?"

"On catching the balls."

"And because they focus on the outcome, they mess up the process and fail to achieve their goal."

"Explained that way, it sounds simple."

"Have you ever hit a bad golf shot?" Lise asked, moving on to an activity that she knew Douglas familiar with.

"Have I ever?" Douglas was caught between hysteria and disbelief. "Too many to recount," he eventually responded.

"See any connection here?"

"The outcome in golf is getting the ball to go where you want it to go."

"And the process?"

"The swing itself. Yes, I can see that when we focus on the outcome we become fearful of where we might put the ball, we begin to doubt our ability and we become filled with anxiety. Most rounds are played against a backdrop of constant fear. The answer is obviously to focus on the swing, and let the outcome look after itself."

"Easier said than done, I guess?" Lise asked, smiling at Douglas.

"Without doubt. And I do know that when I had confidence in myself in the past I was able to establish a clear intention and then focus on the swing itself."

"Watch this – only a very short clip,' Lise said,

turning on the film again to watch a meeting of middle managers that had taken place at the beginning of the financial year.

"These targets are far too high. We've absolutely no chance of achieving them!" Douglas heard a manager say before Lise switched the film off again.

"That was short," said Douglas, surprised that Lise hadn't let him hear the responses.

"They all agreed," Lise said, putting his mind at ease. "So what was the stated intention of the manager?" she asked. "To achieve the target?"

"No, precisely the opposite. He was stating quite clearly that they would not achieve it."

"So where would their attention go with an intention like this?"

"Probably to looking for excuses – their T.T.I.s – for not achieving it."

"Most probably. The challenge here is one that most people face in some context of their life at some time or another, when they are faced with something that seems impossible to achieve. The normal response is similar to the one you just heard, because most people have been conditioned into developing what I call a 'scarcity mentality'."

"Doesn't sound too inspiring," commented Douglas, intrigued to learn more about this mentality.

"It isn't," said Lise, shaking her head. "Most people have been brought up with this belief – that there isn't 'enough' and only a few are capable of really getting what is available. That's why people are seduced into spending money on the National Lottery each week. They see it as the only way to get what they want. I usually remind them that they've already won the lottery – they're alive – and that they should focus more energy on how they 'spend their winnings'."

"Live their lives, in other words?" asked Douglas.

Lise nodded her approval.

"As Dan Millman wrote in Way of the Peaceful Warrior, 'Death is not sad, the sad thing is that most people never really live at all.' Or as Marylin Morris points out in her book Mutant Message Down Under, the indigenous aboriginal tribe known as 'The Real People' believe that 'Because someone is breathing doesn't mean they're alive. It's only on indication of whether they should be buried or not'."

Douglas could recall once or twice noticing how some people who had come into the *Guardian Angel* headquarters had reminded him a bit of the 'living dead'.

"Reminds me of the London Underground at rush hour," said Douglas, deciding to use another example.

"Pretty good analogy," commented Lise, nodding her approval. She understood that Douglas didn't want to be too derogatory about his own people, now he had begun to understand his own part in the whole process.

"So, back to my point about dealing with the seemingly impossible." Lise realised she was in danger of heading off on too big a tangent.

"Rather than say what your manager said about the targets being too high and that they would never reach them, they could say something like, 'These targets are extremely challenging – or high – and we will do all we can to get as close as possible to achieving them'. Where would their attention be placed or focused then?"

"On ways of achieving the targets, or at least getting as close to them as possible."

"Yeah. Having created the intention of going for it, the opportunities begin to appear, almost by magic."

Douglas could relate to this, since there had been many times in his career when opportunities had presented themselves to him after he had made a real commitment.

"You could relate this, to a certain extent, to the opposite of a scarcity mentality. Having an 'abundance mentality' means that we realise that what we want is already out there."

"Out where?" Douglas wasn't sure about this. It was beginning to really challenge him again.

"Out there, as in the universe or the world, if you like."

"You mean it already exists?"

"Yes, or is available to us. This doesn't have to necessarily relate to material outcomes, it can also relate to more spiritual goals, or to how someone wants to feel about themselves and their world. Remember, those who experience a scarcity mentality believe that only a limited few can really access life's real treasures. Those who live with an abundance mentality understand how to connect with what they want, they make a real decision."

"A true intention?"

"Perfect! This, in turn, is a commitment. So many people really believe they have no choice. I've heard people say, for example, 'I hate my job but what else can I do?', implying there is nothing else. They have, one way or another, allowed themselves to be seduced by this belief."

Douglas's mind was racing. This sounded very much like his current predicament. Had he been seduced into believing there was nothing else he could do but sell out *Guardian Angel* to the bank? Was this really some kind of mass hypnosis, perpetrated by those with most to gain?

"Some difficult times and decisions ahead, I suspect." Lise commented, having, of course, picked up Douglas's thoughts.

"That's more than suspicion." Douglas's brow furrowed as he pursed his lips. "That's a definite. And perhaps it would be better to reword that as 'challenging' times and decisions?"

"Touché!" Lise exclaimed, clapping her hands. "Who is the teacher now?"

Douglas felt pleased, confused and worried all at once; pleased that he had woken up to what was possible for himself, his people and the business; confused about having to deal with the conflicting choices ahead; and worried about how he was going to resolve those choices.

"We can all be taken to the door of change: the challenge is that we have to walk through it on our own." Douglas recalled that these were the last words that Lise had spoken to him before she took her leave in the normal way. He had swung round to look out of his window and ponder his dilemma and her words. When he turned back, she had gone.

Douglas suddenly noticed it was beginning to get a little darker and that he and Tara had walked further than they had in a long time. They had reached the point where the stream descended sharply, transforming into a small but powerful 'force'. It must have been the sound of the water that stirred Douglas from his thoughts. Tara was at his side, mouth open, panting a little and looking up at Douglas for approval.

Douglas sat down on a large grey stone that gave him a superb view upstream and of the 'force' itself as it shot the water dramatically downstream. He smiled as he related what he saw now to his own experience over the past few weeks. He had been moving forward smoothly and steadily towards the expected business outcome, insofar as one could in these kinds of complex business negotiations. It was an outcome which entailed *Guardian Angel* becoming part of a major player on the UK and European financial scene, and, in the future, on the global scene. And suddenly things had changed. Just like the water in the stream, Douglas saw that his life had been turned upside down, propelled at great speed and spat out of the other side, possibly to take a whole new direction. He was the same person, only now he was far more conscious. He visualised the picture further downstream, where he remembered the water calming again into a smooth, moving mass of liquid power. His mind now freed up from constant logic and rationality, Douglas visualised the *Guardian Angel* team moving together smoothly and powerfully as one unit, each depending on the other to create the whole. Douglas visualised the business ultimately moving forward, growing in strength and power together: a community of souls achieving success for all concerned. Wow, thought Douglas, what a business that would be. He stood up, stretched his hands up to the sky and headed back home in the twilight, Tara at his heels.

"You're late back again," said Pat to Douglas as he walked in through the back door. She was in the kitchen preparing the evening meal.

"Got caught up in my thoughts again."

"Still agonising over what you should do?"

"Yes, still running through all the options and turning the various arguments over in my mind. I've made mental and written lists of the pros and cons for recommending going ahead with this move so many times, and I'm still undecided."

"What does your intuition tell you?" Pat asked, putting the final touches to a very healthy-looking mixed salad. "You know what I mean – like your own *Guardian Angel*."

"Do you mean, do I have a gut feeling?" Douglas replied.

Pat recognised that Douglas normally made decisions on the basis of the factual information he had available, and that many years in the financial world had dampened his intuition. "Yes, if you want to put it like that."

"Well, it's strange really because it's only over the last month or so that I've begun to be aware of these feelings, as if someone was trying to help me make these decisions."

"And?" Pat turned to face Douglas.

"Ah, you mean what am I being told? I think it is this feeling that is making me reconsider going forward with the sell-out."

"What a horrible term," said Pat, screwing up her face.

"There is definitely a part of me that wants to pull out, and work at taking *Guardian Angel* forward on its own."

"And the other part?"

"That's the logical-rational part which tells me that the take-over is the way to go. That there is no real way forward alone. What is your feeling on it?" Douglas asked Pat.

Pat had finished serving up the food and put both plates on the table ready for them to eat.

"Ultimately that decision has to come from you.

You will know when you really know. Why don't you sleep on it?" Pat suggested, lifting her glass of wine towards Douglas's.

"After I break through a solid gate, clear wind blows from time immemorial."

T'Aego (1310 – 82) Zen Master